The New Fords

The largest manufacturer of tractors in the United Kingdom, the Ford Motor Company, had maintained a high level of production of its model 'N' throughout hostilities. The production line on which this model was produced was well nigh worn out by 1945, but it was not possible to retool and re-equip the plant to launch a completely new model. Firstly, the sophisticated machine tools required to cope with a new engine for such a tractor were not available from UK manufacturers, and spending in dollars was not encouraged. The continued need for tractors meant that the model could not be altered too much if production was to be maintained.

Consultation with the War Agricultural Committees identified the need for a tractor which could haul three furrows instead of two, have a rowcrop capability with higher ground clearance than the 'N', and have a central PTO. In addition the capability of the tractor taking a three point linkage and self starting were added by Fords, although these features did not appear until later. To get the ground clearance and greater power the old worm and wheel transmission of the Fordson were replaced by a new double reduction rear axle with spiral bevel drive on the bull pinion shaft, a feature copied from various US designs. The result was the E27N (E = English; 27 = 27HP; N = Tractor). Some 60% of the parts used in initial production were the same as used by the previous model, a further 10% were N parts with modification, and the final 20% were all new, mainly in the area of the rear axle. There was always one big disadvantage with the E27N, and that was the engine. It was outdated technologically, and this made overhaul a somewhat cumbersome operation. Unlike then current Transatlantic practice, blocks were cast with cylinders en bloc; the connecting rods and main bearings were direct metalled. Quite sophisticated equipment had been developed at the dealers for the overhaul of such engines.

It is all very well prolonging the life of tractors with an obsolete engine, but when the need arises to provide a diesel variant, it may sound strange that the engine manufacturer had more to do with this than the tractor builder. Nevertheless the Perkins P6(TA) engine gave a tractor in the 45HP class which filled a need at the time. Some 236000 Fordson Majors were built from 1945-52, and a high proportion were exported. Headaches occurred for Ford especially in the form of competition from the "Grey Menace" (q.v.) and there were also other manufacturers on the scene by 1950, who although not capable of building as many tractors as Ford, with a good dealer and salesmen in a certain area, could knock holes in home sales. For the full story of the E27N we refer readers to Issue 5 in this series which covers this tractor fully.

Although Ford knew what sort of tractor if would have liked to build in 1945 it was not able to give the machine its proper engine. The E27N was a stopgap. Now engine development is an expensive business. We have to look at what other engines Ford were producing in the late forties to see the way ahead.

Besides the trusty old 4380cc side valve tractor unit inherited from the model 'N' there were the 8 and 10 horsepower small bore units, which found application in som ... the V8 which was not only used in the ... ne, but as a power unit in the Thames series of trucks. If a diesel was required, the Perkins P6V was the unit for the lorries, and the P6(TA) the unit for the tractors.

To cut development costs, an engine was developed which would be able to be used in all types of vehicle. It was also to be capable of being a diesel, petrol, and even a VO unit, and would be built in four and later six cylinder sizes. The type of fuel pump dictated the performance characteristics of the diesel, and the carburettor the performance of the petrol. The six cylinder units did not appear until 1957, and were not initially designed for tractor use but as we will see later they did find some use.

The great advance in engine design which the Ford development boys achieved was a considerable measure of common parts between the spark ignition and compression ignition engines. This again reduced production costs, and helped the parts boys in that it reduced the number of spares one had to carry. As it happened, with something new, the modifications in the first five years of production were to prove somewhat of a parts and service managers nightmare, but for the first time a diesel engine which actually started well and came out at a reasonable cost was to grace many applications.

For not only did Ford fit the engines to their own Thames range of trucks and tractors, but sales of the units for industrial and other use made the E1A engine one of the best sellers of the fifties and early sixties. Just like the old Fordson tractor and the numerous conversions thereof, there was little into which the new range of engines was not put.

As far as the tractor was concerned, it was very much based on the E27N as far as transmission layout was concerned - even the front axle was identical, but skilful redesign of the gearbox (based on the 7.7 High Top Green Spot unit) added a primary box in front and thus gave the tractor 6 forward and two reverse gears. The hydraulics were different, the top PTO was abandoned, and the hydraulic pump installed in the rear transmission driven from the normal PTO and taking its oil supply from the rear axle's 9 gallon capacity. Linkage was very similar to the old E27N, there being no depth control at this stage.

It was in the engines that Ford broke new ground. As already described, three versions were available in the tractor on its launch in November 1951; Diesel, TVO, and Petrol. The diesel and TVO used the same 100mm bore whilst the Petrol was 97mm.

It goes without saying that the Diesel was an instant success and with the TVO engine being somewhat of a fuel guzzler and awkward to start to boot it was the New Fordson Major that firmly established the high speed diesel engine as a prime mover on our farms. From 1952 on the trend was away from low cost fuel engines with the need for separate starting petrol, and if there is a tractor which spelt the death knell of the TVO engine it is the New Fordson Major.

The unit construction went with the E1A model - the engine with its multiple applications was not self stressed and had to be supported by a sub frame in the form of two channels bolted to the sides of the clutch

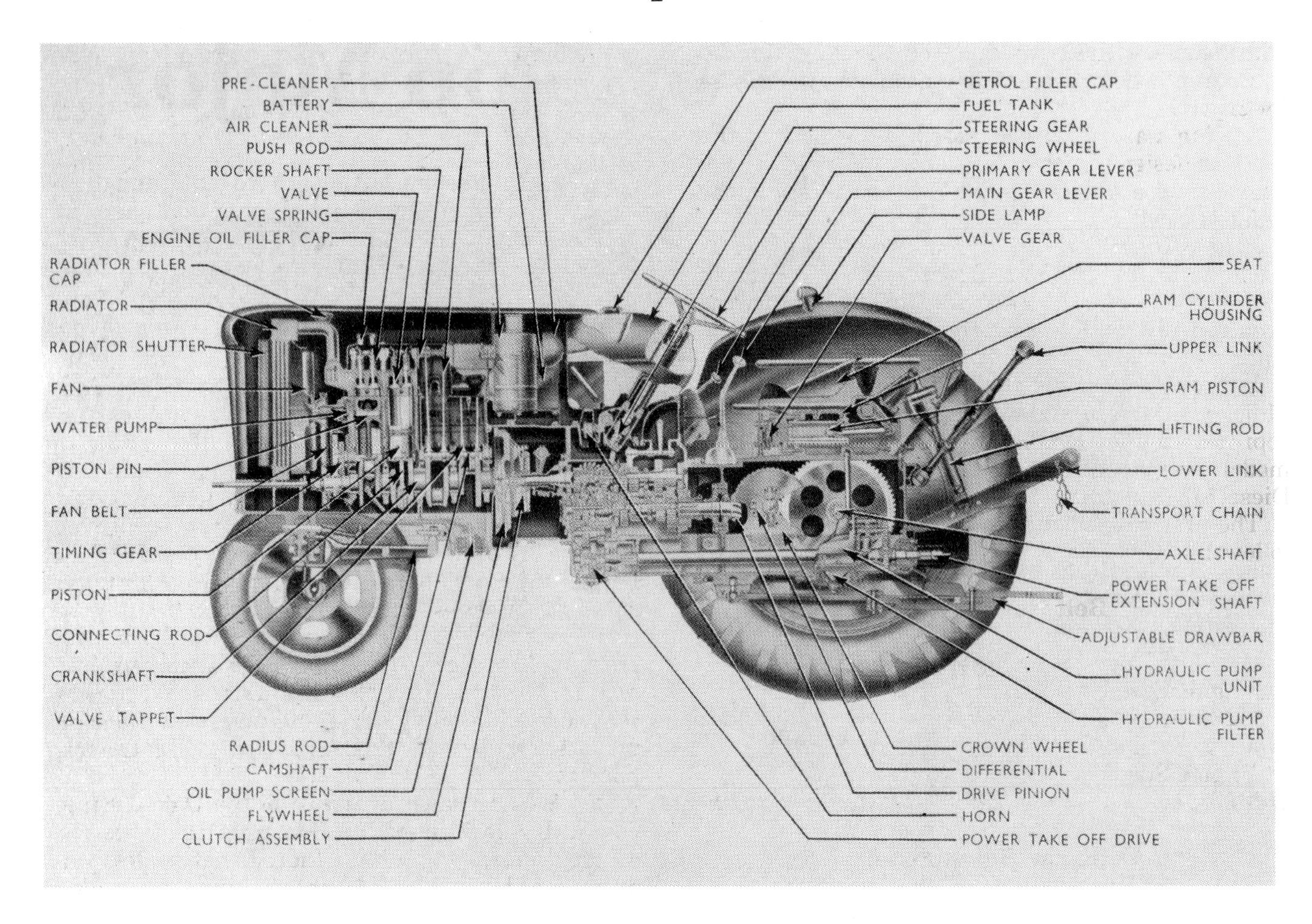

These sectional views show the New Fordson Major (above) and the Fordson Power Major (below). The design was very well thought out and indeed surpasses the complications of present day tractors. Many thousands of these tractors are still in use worldwide.

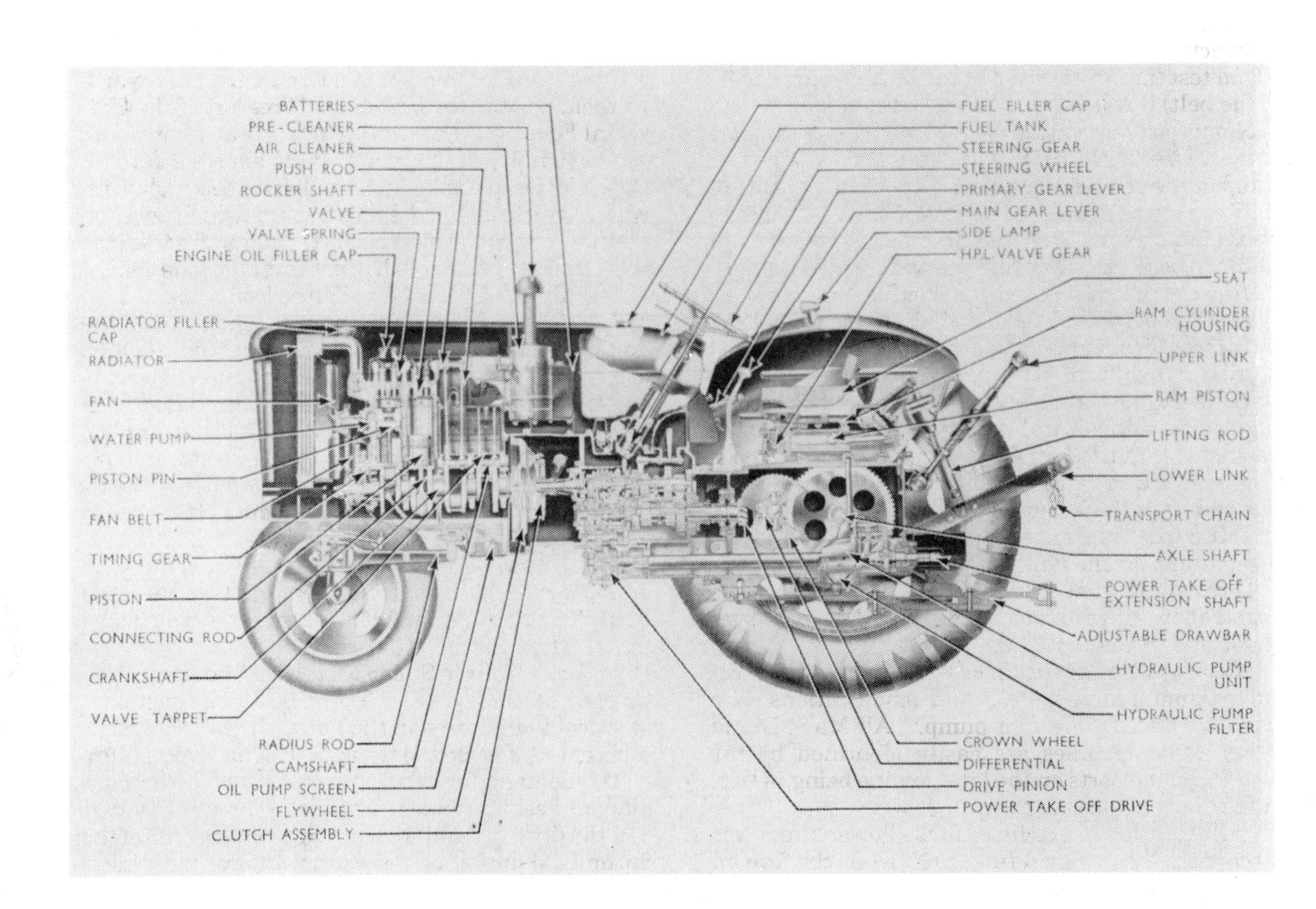

housing, and with its own cast front to take either the usual front axle or a vee twin unit made by Roadless for export.

Styling was attractive, possibly the best of the postwar designs, with a fuel tank to the rear of the engine, and a hinged bonnet between this and the radiator cowl.

A new line was set up to build the New Fordson Major within the Dagenham complex and production soon settled down to a satisfactory level with the eventual proclamation by the sales boys that the tractor was exported to 100 territories!

In the first analysis, the performance of the New Major was not outstanding, but the power output represented a modest increase on the previous TVO model and a considerable decrease on the Perkins Diesel engined unit.

The first published figures for this tractor are as follows:

Belt Horse Power

	Diesel	Petrol	VO
At Engine Speed of 1400rpm	34	33	32
At Engine Speed of 1600rpm	37	35	34

Drawbar Horse Power

	Diesel	Petrol	VO
Max db hp.	29.75	29.0	28.25
Speed mph.	3.40	3.42	3.44

As can be seen, these figures were not anything special. Indeed with the E27N capable of 26.6 for a VO tractor, and the P6 engined E27N recording 34/41 HP on test (i.e. 34 at the drawbar in 2nd gear, and 41 at the belt) it was a bit of a comedown!

Numerous modifications were made to the engine in the years 1952 - 1956, and details of these can be found in the second section of this book, but it was in 1957 that the engine was updated, from 1425097 in April of that year. This had the effect of giving more power - the interesting thing is that the tractors so fitted were not advertised. To confuse the issue an industrial engine had been available from early 1957 with a modified manifold which allowed engine speed to peak at 1800rpm. This was carried over onto the Mark II engines from 1425097 but was not recommended for agricultural use. What was so amazing was that the Mark II engine was not generally advertised! At the same time the TVO model was quietly dropped. It had taken just five years to firmly establish the compression ignition engine as the main power plant for the Fordson tractor.

The main reasons for modifying the engine was as a prelude to things to come, for in July 1958 the Power Major was introduced.

This was rated at 51.8BHP @ 1600rpm. To effect the maximum increase in power modifications were made to the fuel injection pump. All Mark II and Power Major engines are easily identified by the manifolds, the ports on the later engine being in line, the earlier engine staggered.

Indeed, the engine as fitted to the Power Major was to remain the same until June 1962, when the fitment of the Simms Minimec pump and mechanical governor raised the BHP to 53.7.

The Power Major also differed from the New Major in several other ways. The 'live PTO' option had in fact come in with the New Major with tractor 1417988 in February 1957, but the main alterations to the new model apart from the engine output centred around a higher driving position with instrument panel below the steering column and a conveniently located throttle lever also mounted below the steering column. New style wheel centres were also featured.

We need now, however, to return to the age old problem facing the Ford Sales Team, the "Grey Menace". No matter how successful the "New Major" was, there was still the 'light' end of the market which, in the mid fifties, was a wholly Ferguson preserve.

Ford in the USA had concentrated, with considerable success, on the 'light' end of the market starting with the 8N which was in essence an improved "Ford Fergie". Circumstances dictated that, in order to get out of the "nasties" over the Ferguson patents, that very successful 8N Dearborn tractor which after all accounted for over 400000 units in its 4 year run, had to be replaced. Indeed, the very fact that Ferguson's own Detroit line only built 140000 units over the same period shows just how Ford could always beat the rest hands down.

The 8N was never available in the United Kingdom, although some got into Southern Ireland, as did its replacement the NAA. Indeed that model, produced for the Jubilee of Ford, featured an engine driven hydraulic pump and other details which even the British built equivalent, when it arrived, did not have.

By far the most expensive item to develop on any tractor is the engine. Now the very engine which Ford were using in the fifties range was a non stressed unit common with truck production which, in the tractors, required a sub frame for additional strength. Ideally, a three cylinder version of same in the way which Nuffield created the Universal Three out of the Universal Four would have been ideal. But what would you have finished up with? Quite simply a derated Diesel Major, possibly with smaller wheels and tyres, with complete lack of the very features which 'sold' the Ferguson. It would have been very attractive from the parts and service angle but not from the sales one.

The tractor had to be a 'Fergie look alike'. This would involve the use of a stressed engine so that the unit construction could be maintained, and the high beam type front axle with dual track rod steering employed. The weight of a reduced 'Major' viz a viz an 8N derived machine would also be at a disadvantage. The subsequent development of the Dexta, is however, another story which will be covered in a future 'special'. And we must now move out of the smaller end of the market to resume the story of the Fordson Major. The Power Major had the shortest life span of any model built at Dagenham, and by the time Smithfield Show in 1960 came along, a revised model was on show there.

In fact the first Super Major was built on 24th October of that year. The engine was virtually identical to that used in the Power Major. The main differences affected the transmission and hydraulics.

The demand for extra grip to cope with the handling of heavier implements now coming into vogue saw the fitting of a differential lock, and instead of the faithful old dual shoe self energising slewing brakes inherited from the E27N, disc units were now employed, and back in the original brake location hard against the transmission housing. On previous New Majors and Power Majors bull pinion extensions were provided to minimise oil leakage. The designers now put their trust in current oilseal technology.

United Kingdom Patents on the Ferguson Draft Control had expired for some time before they were applied to the Major. The Super Major featured a new hydraulic unit with draft control - Ford called their system "Position Control/Qualitrol". At last the Ferguson draft control was breaking out of its designers insistence on its application to light tractors only, and the robust unit fitted to the 'Super' retained the same characteristics of its predecessor, with the improved design gear type hydraulic pump driven from the PTO shaft, and drawing its oil supply from the rear transmission. The introduction of 'universal' oils aided the operation of the unit considerably, especially in low ambient temperatures.

The appearance of the 'Super' was further changed by the fitting of the headlamps within the two front grille panels, although this configuration only appeared on domestic agricultural models - the old side mounted lights plus a new style of front grille panel with pressed reinforcement bars was used on some export and industrial units.

In the world of diesel engines there was a general move away from pneumatic governing, and from April 1962 Fordson Major engines featured the Simms 'Minimec' fuel injection pump with mechanical governor built in as an extension of the pump body.

By June 1963 work was well advanced on the integration of all Ford tractor designs to produce the 'Worldwide' range. The engine plant at Dagenham which produced the four and six cylinder engines for trucks and tractors was reaching the end of its economic life, and in any case tractor production would be moved in 1964 to the new Basildon operation.

Nevertheless, tractor production had to be maintained and models still updated to satisfy an expanding market. The 'Super Major' was given its last 'facelift' and with some modifications to the engine in the area of the camshaft and valves gave a greater output at 53.7BHP. One of the inherent weaknesses with the Fordson Major was is poor ground speed PTO capability, and this saw gear ratios altered to improve performance when running with PTO driven implements, especially pick-up balers.

The Spanish Connection

1964 was not the end of the road for the Super Major. Motor Iberica SA was founded in 1920 to build Fords in Spain. The Franco regime nationalised Ebro as it was better known in 1954. In 1964 the tooling and jigs for the manufacture of the New Fordson Major were shipped to the Spanish factory and production of the tractor commenced there under licence in 1965. The tractor was virtually identical to the final New Performance Super Major but had an extended air intake stack and was badged as the Ebro Super 55.

Following an agreement with the Spanish Massey Ferguson and Perkins concessionaires in 1966 the tractor continued in production, but by 1968 it was being offered as the Ebro 155. From a distance the tractor looked very much like any other 100 series Massey Ferguson but under the 'new' tinwork the old Super Major was still there in its entirety.

In the early 1970s Ebro looked outside Spain to sell surplus production and a restyled version of the 155 with revised front cowling to remove the MF likeness was launched as the 160E. Attempts were made to market this model in the USA through Farmax of Mobile, Alabama, and also in the United Kingdom.

The story does not end there, however, as the good old Fordson Major transmission was mated up to a Perkins 6.305 engine to produce the 684E in the early seventies. Then, the Perkins 4.236 engine was fitted to the same transmission and the Ebro 470 appeared. Finally, the Perkins A4.248 engine was fitted to produce the Ebro 480. So we almost return to the 1950s when Perkins L4(TA) conversions were a popular way of getting more power out of the original New Fordson Major.

W. Harold Perry of Potters Bar, Middlesex, imported a number of Ebro engines into the UK where they were sold as replacements both in Ford trucks and Fordson tractors, indeed one Doe triple D is known to exist today with a pair of these engines fitted.

The Conversions.

The E27N Major found favour with a number of conversions specialists, and was used as the basis for a wide variety of machinery. Many of these specialists, plus a number of new users, took the New Major and adapted it into a multitude of machinery.

Firstly, we will look at the simple tractor conversions carried out.

There was obviously a need for a crawler model of the E1A tractor, and County Commercial Cars provided a similar crawler to that based on the E27N. This developed along with the development of the New Major through the Power and Super models, so that the final versions were more 'disguised' than the original one, with specific versions aimed at the agricultural and industrial markets. A short lived model was the 'Fourdrive' which was in effect the crawler tractor with tracks replaced by four equal sized wheels; those on the front being driven by roller chains enclosed in a steel case. This model had limited popularity because of its 'skid' steering. The development of the County Super Four model brought true equal wheel four-wheel drive to the Fordson Super Major. The application of the six cylinder engine to this model gave the 'Super Six'. In time 4WD models took over in the County range and following the move to the Ford 6X models a crawler was no longer offered by County.

Roadless Traction, whose DG pattern half-tracks were available for the New Major, had a sojourn into full tracks with their J17 model. By far the biggest influence on tractor development, not only on Fordson units, was their marketing and building of 4WD units using the design of transfer gearbox and front axle pioneered by Selene SAS in Italy. They were initially marketed as 'Manuel-Roadless' units, but when the patents expired Roadless continued to build similar units under its own name.

The great advantage of the Roadless units were that they could be fitted to existing tractors without difficulty. Sales continued right up till 1964, and the

Initial estimates regarding the popularity of the spark ignition models were totally wrong and in due course there were very few being built, indeed this 1955 example was one of only 10% of production in that year built with TVO or petrol engines.

Roadless Ploughmaster 6/4 was also offered with six cylinder engine.

Other firms dabbled with 4WD, one of those worth a mention was Matbro, who built their 'Mastiff' using two Fordson Super Major rear transmission units. The 'Dual drive' and later 'Triple -D' units from Ernest Doe used two tractors coupled together to give a 100HP unit. The idea was that the two tractors united could be used for heavy ploughing in the winter, and be separated into two for use in the harvest in summer. In fact few tractors were used in this way and as the model developed more control of the front unit hydraulically was achieved. The whole ensemble was coupled together by a turntable which linked both units, and power steering was provided.

Other conversions were made for special uses. The Kent Ford Dealers' syndicate produced two 'narrow' versions of 52" and 68" overall width. Whilst a tricycle version of the New Major was sold in overseas territories with Roadless supplied vee front wheel equipment, for the UK market it was left to Bettinsons of Holbeach and others to provide a single front wheel conversion. County also provided a High Clearance version for export.

We now move to the 'Industrial' side of the market. Chase-Side Engineering continued to build their rope operated shovels on New Major skid units, and Muir-Hill offered their SSD Loader which also used winch drive. The upsurge of hydraulic equipment brought forth loading shovels from Weatherill, Whitlock, Bray, Muir-Hill, Chase-Side, and J. C. Bamford. The application of the back-hoe to some units brought us the 'Dinkum Digger' and finally the JCB, whose fame is such that all loader/backhoe units nowadays tend to be described in common language as such. JCB units are fully covered in 'Vintage Tractor Special - 12 ; JCB 1945-1980'.

It is a known fact that by the mid 1950s Ford had totally captured the 'skid unit' market in the United Kingdom (and in part overseas), with build varying from an engine and bonnet to complete tractors. Perkins suffered badly from the success of the New Major engine, expressly the diesel version which of course became almost universal after 1957. Other uses for the engine alone were on Road Pavers (Barber Greene), Compressors, Vibrating Rollers, Mobile Cranes, Generating sets, etc. etc.

As part of the sales drive to woo the conversion specialists, Ford provided a reverse crown wheel and pinion build of skid for the mid fifties generation of loading shovels which operated 'face about'. Later a torque convertor transmission was offered.

Muir-Hill were always a strong user of Ford units, and throughout the 1950s they offered their 10B dumper based on the New Major with a variety of bodies. It has only been possible to illustrate the most basic of conversions in this volume; a later issue will cover the diverse conversions applied to E27N and E1A tractors.

We will now look at the cost of buying the New Major and some derivatives as at mid 1955.

New Fordson Major Rowcrop:

Petrol.	£441. 15. 0
TVO.	£441. 15. 0
Diesel	£496. 5. 0

The above prices included starter and steering brakes. Extras were: Belt Pulley £8.10.0.; PTO £12.0.0.; Hydraulics £60.0.0.; Electric Lighting £7.11.0.

KFD Narrow model 52 (54"width)

Diesel.	£597. 10. 0
TVO	£543. 0. 0

KFD Narrow model 68 (68"width)

Diesel.	£544. 10. 0
TVO	£490. 0. 0

County. Mark II with 12" tracks.

Diesel.	£1195. 0. 0
do with 14" tracks	£1198. 0. 0
do with 16" tracks	£1203. 0. 0

(Petrol and TVO versions were available to special order at £54. 10s less cost.

County. Fourdrive.

Diesel	£1500. 0. 0

Opposite page; top and centre. Two illustrations, possibly of one of the three spark ignition tractors built in 1951. Note such long forgotten details as the radiator shutter lever in the lower illustration, the lack of handbrake, and clean bonnet lines with 'hidden' pre-cleaner and underswept exhaust.

Opposite page; bottom. A 1953 Diesel (E1ADDN) model with alternative wheel and tyre equipment (7.50x16" fronts, 14x30" rears) and vertical exhaust. Note the 'Diesel' bonnet embelishment below the usual 'Fordson Major' one.

Above: Rows of tractors await shipment at Dagenham in early 1952 - note the remains of E27N production parked to the right background of the picture; the cloud of smoke is obviously from a P6 engined E27N being started prior to loading for shipment.

Below: An early diesel model ploughing. Note the first pattern mudguards.

Above: If one desired, steel wheels were still available on the New Major. These were the same cast Ford front ones and Sankey made rear ones as used on the E27N.

Right: The commercial tractor was a far simpler specification than its E27N predecessor, from which it inherited the rear wheel brakes and automatic hitch. Note the fitment of a handbrake at a time when this was optional on Agricultural models.

Below: For the US market, vee twin front wheels were available. These components were actually made by Roadless Traction, but were fitted during assembly to export machines. The New Fordson Major became a good dollar earner, becoming a popular machine on the other side of the Atlantic, and eventually gaining the claim of being exported to over 100 territories.

Left: By late 1954 the need for a starting handle had all but been eliminated by the virtual monopoly of the Diesel model on sales. From this period the primary aircleaner was now externally located on all models.

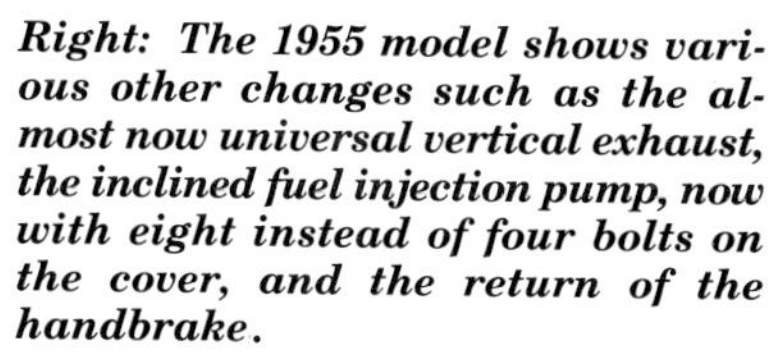

Right: The 1955 model shows various other changes such as the almost now universal vertical exhaust, the inclined fuel injection pump, now with eight instead of four bolts on the cover, and the return of the handbrake.

Left: The bonnet ornament featuring the word Diesel appeared also in late 1954, and can be seen on this diesel (E1ADDN) model ploughing in 1955.

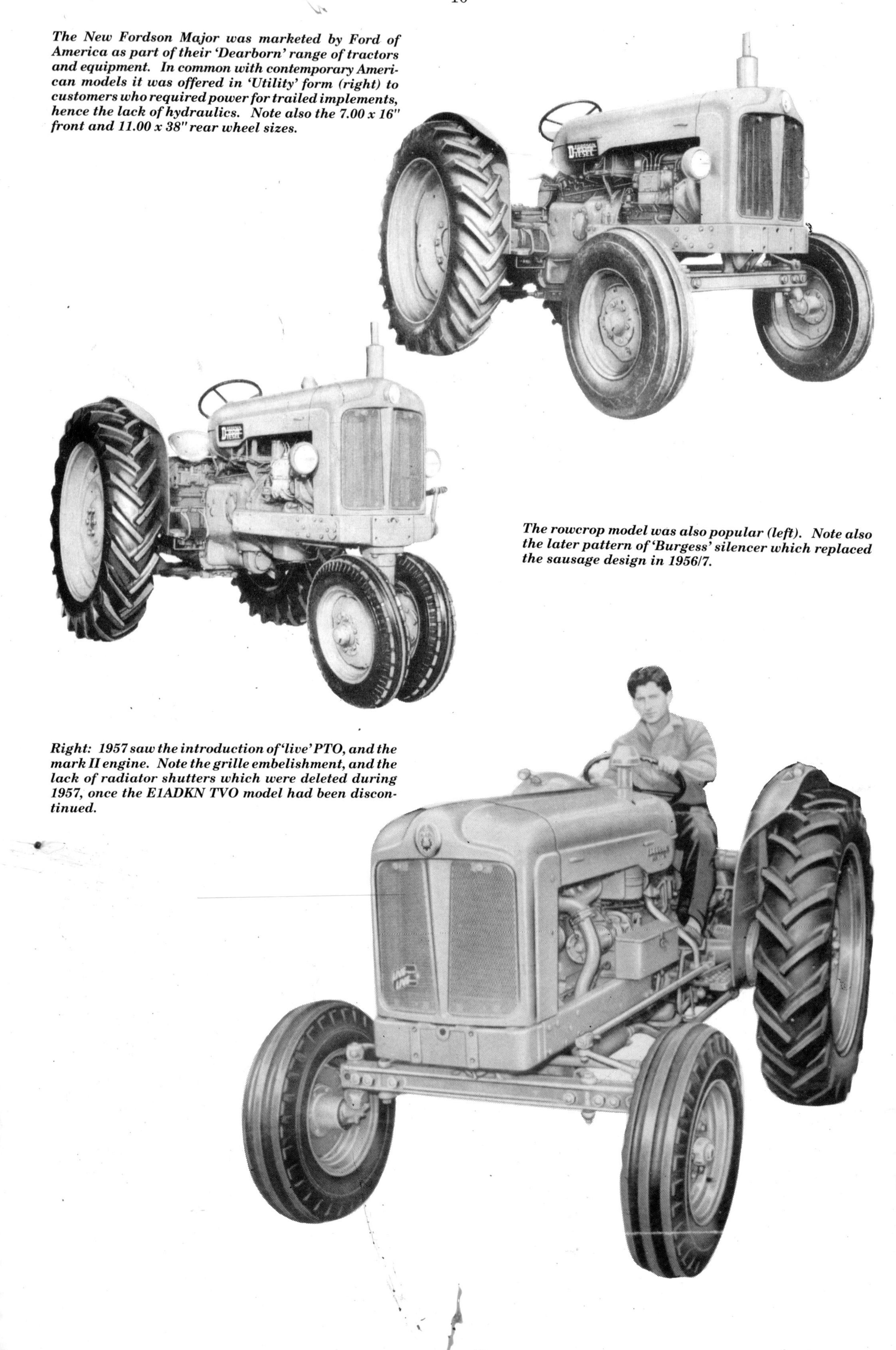

The New Fordson Major was marketed by Ford of America as part of their 'Dearborn' range of tractors and equipment. In common with contemporary American models it was offered in 'Utility' form (right) to customers who required power for trailed implements, hence the lack of hydraulics. Note also the 7.00 x 16" front and 11.00 x 38" rear wheel sizes.

The rowcrop model was also popular (left). Note also the later pattern of 'Burgess' silencer which replaced the sausage design in 1956/7.

Right: 1957 saw the introduction of 'live' PTO, and the mark II engine. Note the grille embelishment, and the lack of radiator shutters which were deleted during 1957, once the E1ADKN TVO model had been discontinued.

Above and Left: The 1958 introduction of the Power Major saw a revised driving position with the instrument panel and throttle lever grouped beneath the steering column.

Right: The Super Major soon replaced the Power Major in 1960, and featured a number of improvements, including Diff. Lock, headlamps recessed into the front grilles, and improved hydraulics incorporating the Ferguson draft control, patents on which had now expired; but with 'Position control/Qualitrol' facility to override the draft facility. Power rating was 51.8BHP @ 1600RPM.

***Above:** The New Performance Super Major was introduced in June 1963 and featured greater engine output (53.7BHP). The engine featured the Simms 'Minimec' fuel injection pump with mechanical governor previously introduced in April 1962. The hydraulics were improved by the addition of a flow control, and gear ratios were also altered to give better ground speed for PTO work. The colour scheme was now blue and grey.*

A front end loader with the New Performance Super Major could be controlled by the addition of a single auxiliary services control which bolted on the side of the normal hydraulic control lever, or a separate dual auxiliary services unit which fitted on top of the nearside rear axle shaft.

Ford in the USA had embarked on the first phase of product consolidation in 1962 when the existing 600 and 800 ranges were updated and given new blue and cream paint schemes to become the 2000 and 4000 ranges. The Super Major was given the same blue and cream paint scheme and sold as the Ford Diesel 5000. Note the power steering.

Above: The Roadless DG4 tracks continued to be available for the New Fordson Major; these were improved in 1953 to become the DG15 tracks, and another option available from this date was the application of 28" front wheels for use on rough terrain (right).

Left: A New Fordson Major with Roadless-McGibbon conversion using an Atkinson spreader. The driving position was moved alongside the engine.

Right: Roadless Traction only produced a handful of full tracked E27N crawlers of the type 'E', but revised their rubber jointed track design to produce the J17 model in 1954.

Left: Four wheel drive originated on the E27N in Italy, where Selene SAS fitted front axles recovered from surplus GM 4WD military vehicle spares. Roadless became licensees for this equipment in due course and the resultant machine is seen here. A sandwich box between gearbox and rear axle took the drive via a propellor shaft to the offset front differential.

Above: A late Roadless equipped 'Super Major' with power assisted steering.

Left: Export 'Super Major' tractors often featured outboard headlamps, as can be seen on this blue/orange example with Roadless 4WD.

Below: A Blue/Grey 'Super Major' with Roadless 4WD and rear mounted winch.

Left and Below: The Roadless Ploughmaster 6/4 was a six cylinder engined unit assembled by Roadless Traction at Hounslow using the Ford 590E diesel - the six cylinder version of the E1A engine. Only a few units were built, some being finished in a green and yellow colour scheme. The excessive engine weight over the front axle caused more than a few problems.

Left: The so called 'Rowcrop' model was not marketed in the United Kingdom and it was left to Bettinsons of Holbeach to produce a single front wheel conversion for use in the potato district of Lincolnshire.

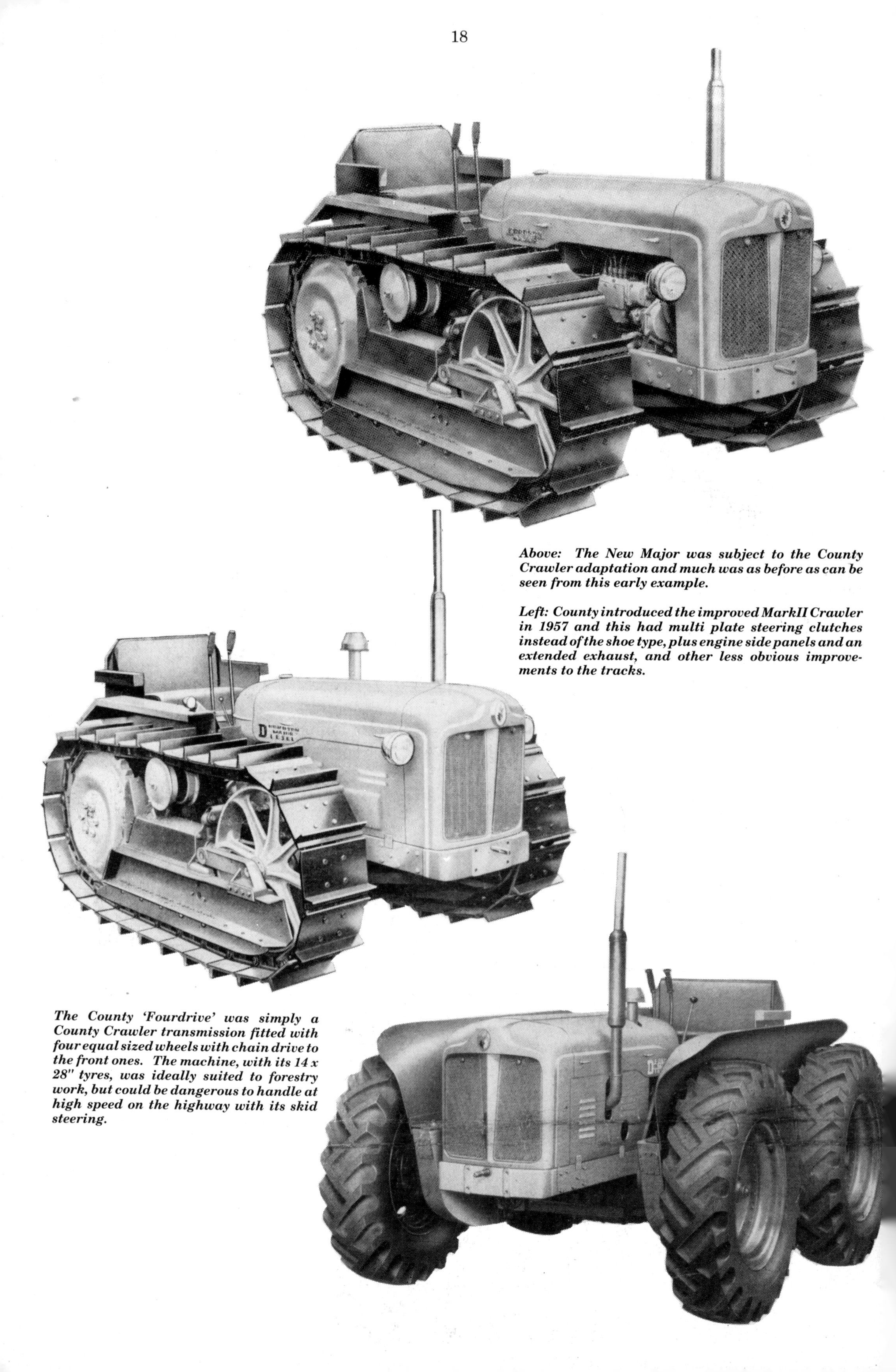

Above: The New Major was subject to the County Crawler adaptation and much was as before as can be seen from this early example.

Left: County introduced the improved MarkII Crawler in 1957 and this had multi plate steering clutches instead of the shoe type, plus engine side panels and an extended exhaust, and other less obvious improvements to the tracks.

The County 'Fourdrive' was simply a County Crawler transmission fitted with four equal sized wheels with chain drive to the front ones. The machine, with its 14 x 28" tyres, was ideally suited to forestry work, but could be dangerous to handle at high speed on the highway with its skid steering.

***Left:** It was still possible to buy County Crawlers right up until the end of 1964, and here is a late version the CD50 complete with bonnet and sump guards, and special air pre-cleaner for dusty conditions.*

***Right:** County also produced this high clearance model which had special rear axle housings driving the rear wheels by a train of three gears, to give an overall ground clearance of 30". Most of these units went to Thompson of USA for conversion into Cane units.*

***Left:** A simpler track conversion was the application of 'Bombardier' halftracks as seen here.*

Right: County brought in equal wheel 4 wheel drive with the Super Four, and this had split drive to each front wheel taken from the bull pinion housings on each side of the tractor. As the Super Major had a differential lock, this gave diff. lock on both front and rear wheels.

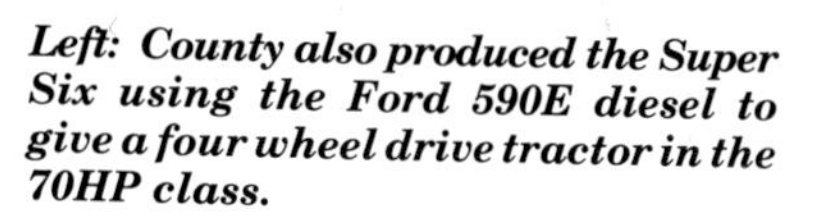

Left: County also produced the Super Six using the Ford 590E diesel to give a four wheel drive tractor in the 70HP class.

Below: JCB had the concession in the UK for these half tracks and a more extreme conversion is seen here with skis instead of front wheels for use on ice or snow.

Kent Ford Dealers low height conversion is seen here; this is the model 68 (left) which was the less drastic conversion of the two; the model 54 (above) seen with a standard tractor featured reduced axle housings to give a narrow track; both had special front axle equipment.

Below: The Howard Trencher was another unit based on the Fordson Major. To provide slow travelling speeds whilst at work a creeper gearbox was sandwiched between the tractor gearbox and rear axle. The example shown is interesting in the fact that the power unit is a Perkins L4(TA).

The Doe 'Triple D' started life as the less sophisticated 'Dual Power' which consisted of two 'Power Majors' joined together to give a 100HP machine. Control of the front tractor was in the main mechanical on the early models, and not all functions were controllable from the rear unit.

The Super Major based unit below was far more sophisticated with hydraulic control of throttle, gearchange, and starter. It was intended that the unit could be converted back to two tractors for summer use but in fact few farmers did this.

At a mere 38BHP the New Fordson Major actually developed less power than its P6 engined predecessor, a feature that was not addressed until the introduction of the Mark II engine in 1957. In the meantime Frank Perkins Ltd. of Peterborough cashed in on the indifferent performance of the TVO (E1ADKN) model and provided, from 1953, a conversion pack using the new L4(TA) engine which developed 47BHP. This was the prototype for the L4 conversion, seen in Milton Street, Peterborough, outside the Perkins factory. Many contractors bought up the TVO tractors at farm and machinery sales and had L4s fitted; with the advent of the Ford MkII engine not only did contractors carry on converting using Ford engines, but dealers often 'dieselised' a TVO tractor to enhance its second-hand sale value.

Above: Motor Iberica was founded to build Ford vehicles in Spain in 1920, but was nationalised by the Franco regimé in 1954. In 1965 production of the New Fordson Major was transferred to Spain where it was marketed as the Ebro Super 55.

Below: Following a tie up with the Spanish M-F and Perkins Companies in 1966, the model was still produced, but was restyled with Massey Ferguson 100 style bonnet and renamed the Ebro 155.

Above: When Ebro set its sights on the export market in the early seventies the 155 was restyled to give it a 'non MF' appearance and finished in Blue and Silver. Note also the restyled fenders and front axle.
Centre: By fitting a Perkins 4.236 engine giving 71BHP @ 2100 RPM, to the basic unit the Ebro 470 produced a further hybrid which was built until the mid 1980s. Shades of the conversion on page 23?
Bottom: With a 6.305 engine installed giving 82BHP @ 2100RPM, you had the Ebro 684E, still with the faithful Fordson Major transmission. It would appear that none of the Spanish variants incorporated transmission handbrakes. We would welcome further information on Ebro tractors from readers.

The Development of the New Fordson Major 1951-58/ Fordson Power Major 1958-60/ Fordson Super Major 1960-62/ New Fordson Super Major 1962-64.

Front Axle and Front Wheels.

From the start only one front axle assembly was available, the fixed variety on the Standard Agricultural and Land Utility variants from the E27N being discontinued on the grounds of economy; the adjustable Rowcrop axle being inherited from that model with a few modifications. The front axle was a heavy steel casting, a single centre beam was bolted to two outer beams which could be repositioned to alter the track from 48" to 72". The front wheels were carried on similar taper roller bearings to the previous model. The track rod ends were of a revised design to give greater clearance under the sub-frame. The steel wheel and pneumatic centres were, in fact, identical, to the units fitted to the model 'E27N'. The pneumatic tyre size was of course 6.00 x 19". Optional 6.50 x 16" front wheels with separate hubs were also available to special order. With the advent of the Power Major the front centre casting was altered from four segmental holes to three.

A vee twin front wheel assembly (made for Ford by Roadless) was available on export tractors and this mounted 6.50 x 16" wheels.

The rear wheels were retained on the rear axle shaft by six studs and nuts. The Standard Agricultural had steel rimmed rears 9" wide mounting 24 spade lugs. The Rowcrop had Sankey type pressings mounting 11.00 x 36" rims with eight locating lugs adjustable by juxtaposition of rim and centre. Again other options were available for export or to special order, and these included 14 x 30" rear wheels with non adjustable centres, and 11.00 x 38" rims which fitted the standard Sankey centre pressings. Scalloped centre discs were introduced with the Power Major which allowed for easier adjustment. The old style Rowcrop 4½" steel rims with extensions were also available as an option and required the old style ten locating lugs, for which a special 11 x 36" rim was also available. Wheels were always orange until the 'grey' of the New Performance Super Major in 1963.

Tractors supplied to Australia were shipped out CKD. either with steel wheels or less wheels. Where pneumatic tyres were fitted these were of different sizes to those used in the United Kingdom, and had distinctive centres. The normal sizes were: 7.50 x 20" on the front and 14 x 28" on the rear but other options to suit local conditions were available.

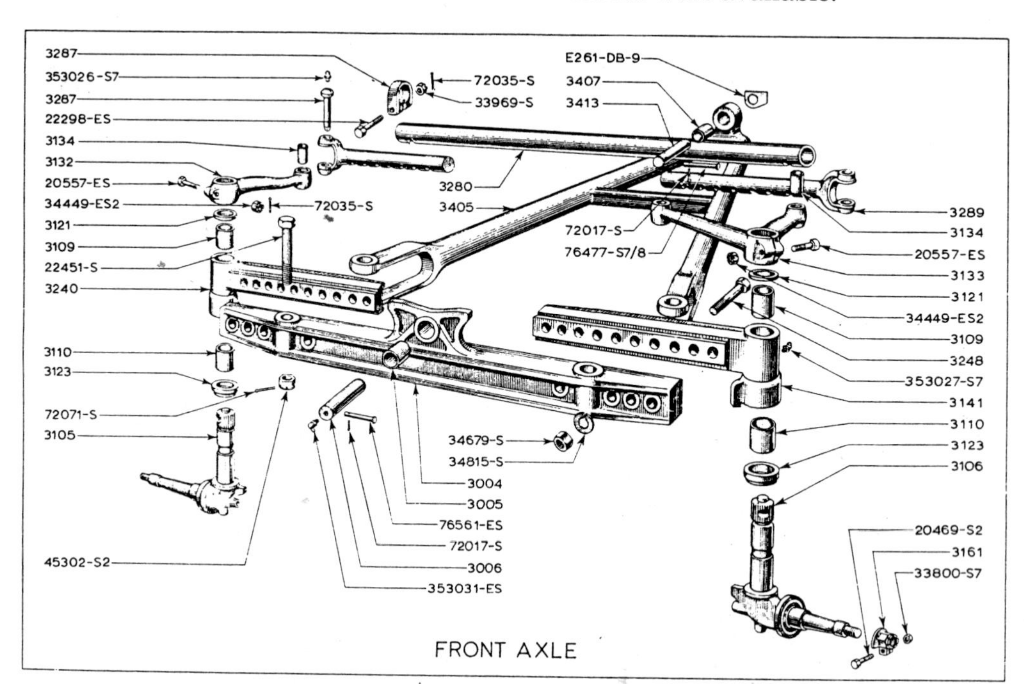

Left: The E1A front axle was based on the E27N unit.

Below: Front wheels: the trusted steel fronts from the 'N' era were still available as were pressed centres with separate hubs for 16" tyres and a cast centre for 19" tyres, the latter shown here being the later version used from 'Power Major' days onward.

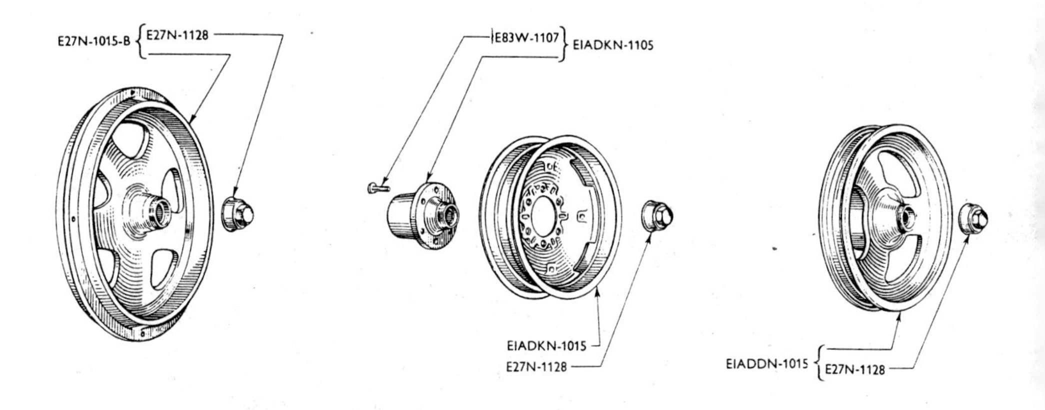

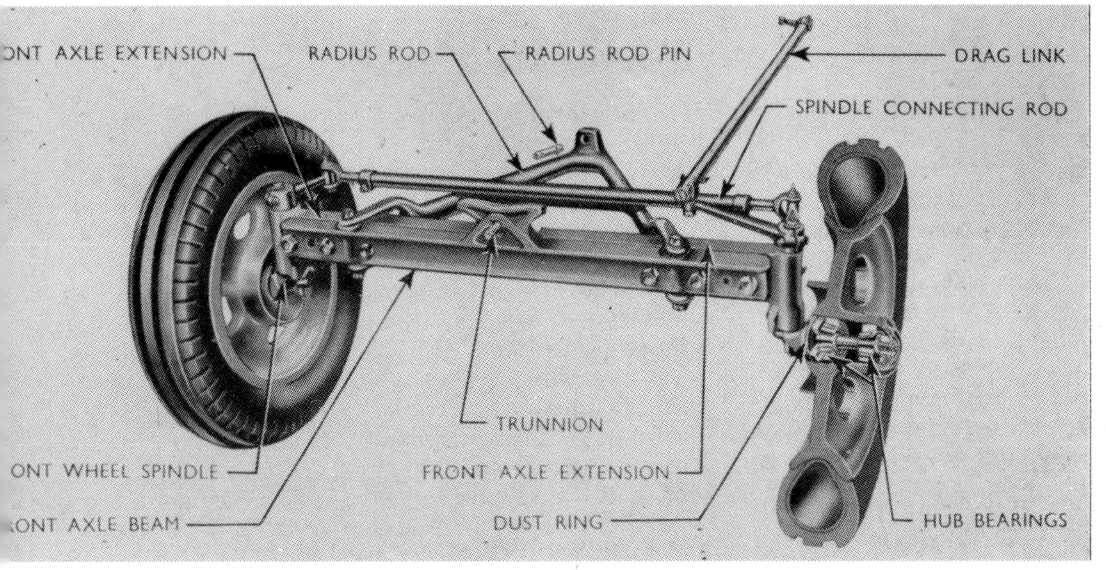

Above: The front axle.

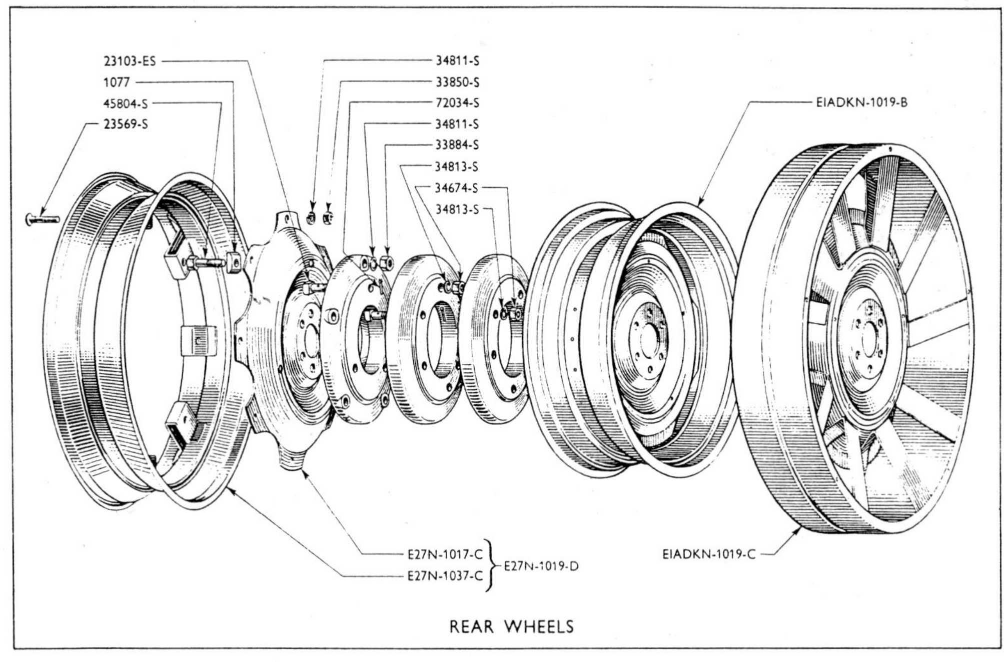

Above: GKN Sankey provided the rear wheel equipment for the New Fordson Major and the rim for mounting 11.00 x 36" tyres is seen on the left. The new 'scalloped' centres introduced with the 'Power Major' are seen next, then the pressed centre for 30" tyres; finally the centre for fixed tread steel wheels which normally mounted spade lugs.

Below: The dual shoe self energising brakes of the New Fordson Major were inherited from the E27N but the bull shafts were extended to try and eliminate oil leakage.

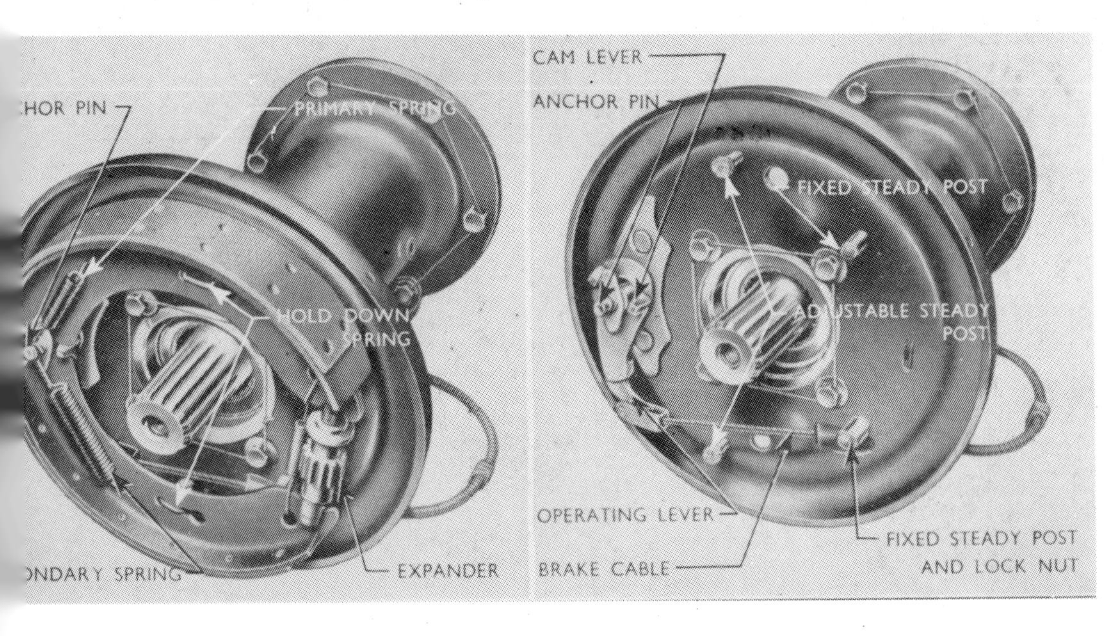

Brakes

The Agricultural and Rowcrop were fitted with independent steering brakes on the ends of the bull pinion shafts; the basic design of brake assembly being inherited from the E27N. These were self energising, cable operated units, the foot pedals being mounted on the right side of the transmission housing, and capable of being locked together for use on the road, and locked down to provide a parking brake. The original type of lock down device was unsatisfactory, and a revised arrangement was fitted from tractor 1235912 in September 1952 which lasted until the end of production. The advantage of using these dual shoe brakes on the countershaft rather than the rear axle is explained by the fact that the bull pinion shafts revolve five times faster than the rear axle shaft, and the use of almost standard automotive components resulted, and the added advantage that the leverage provided positive 'locking' when using the brakes for steering assistance. Oil leakage from the bull pinion shafts onto the brakes was something which was never completely cured on the E27N, hence the extensions adopted on the New Fordson Major.

The Industrial tractor used brakes fitted onto the rear axle shafts; a single pedal was provided.

With the introduction of the Super Major the dual shoe brakes were replaced by disc brakes, and the bull pinion shaft extensions omitted; a revised design of brake pedal was also fitted.

A vacuum brake installation was available as an option for industrial applications.

Transmission Brake

The gearbox contained provision for the same transmission brake as the Fordson 'E27N', but early tractors had this feature omitted except under special order, but the brake plates were still installed inside the gearbox. It was soon found desirable to reintroduce the handbrake and tractors from 1954 had the option reversed, that is to say the lack of handbrake was to special order only, and tractors without did not have the brake components installed in the gearbox. The handbrake lever was mounted on the right side of the transmission housing and was much shorter than the equivalent E27N one.

Steering Gear

The New Major steering gear was a radical departure from previous models in that it was of the Recirculatory Ball type. With the advent of the Power Major the shaft and column were increased in length and flanges added to the column to support the throttle control rod. For export to certain territories a special heavy duty assembly with modified rocker shaft was fitted.

A Power Assisted Steering kit was available and this was fitted as standard equipment to tractors sold in the USA from around 1962. The pump was belt driven from the crankshaft pulley.

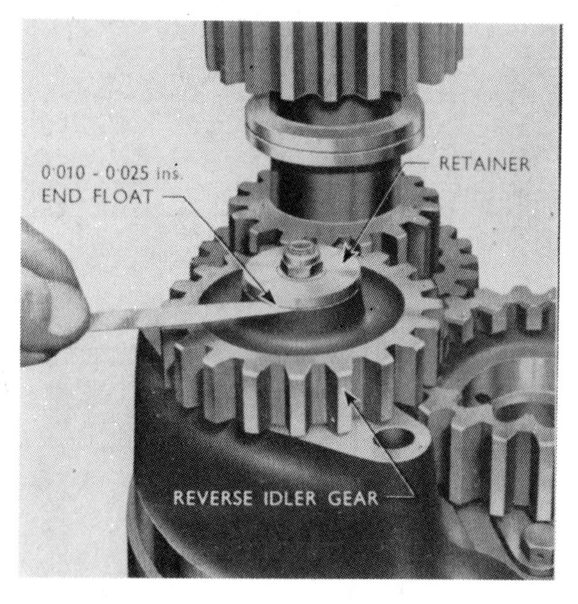

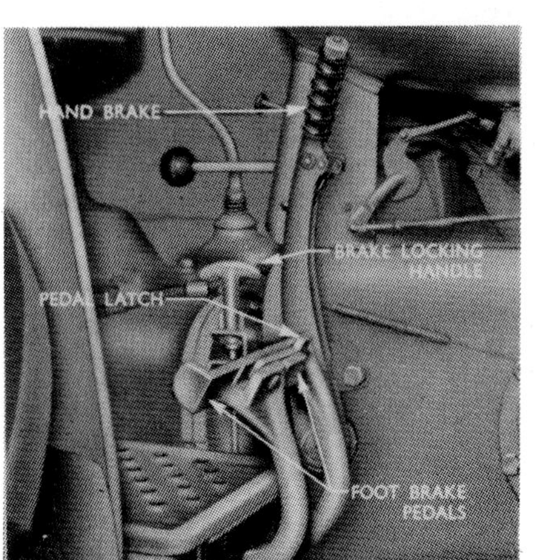

***Above left:** Initial production retained the transmission brake plates inside the gearbox; however the post 1954 assembly is seen here without such complexities.*
***Above Right:** The transmission brake, when fitted, used design features which were unchanged from the 1920s. The 1929 Fordson adopted a brake with 7 stationary and 5 revolving plates and this assembly continued unchanged until the end of E1A production in 1964. Spanish built tractors lacked the transmission brake.*
***Left:** The original brake lock-down assembly was soon modified from a less than satisfactory lever catch to the style shown here.*
***Opposite page:** Exploded views of the braking system used until 1960 (top), the disc brakes used from 1960-64 (centre), and the recirculatory ball type steering employed (bottom).*

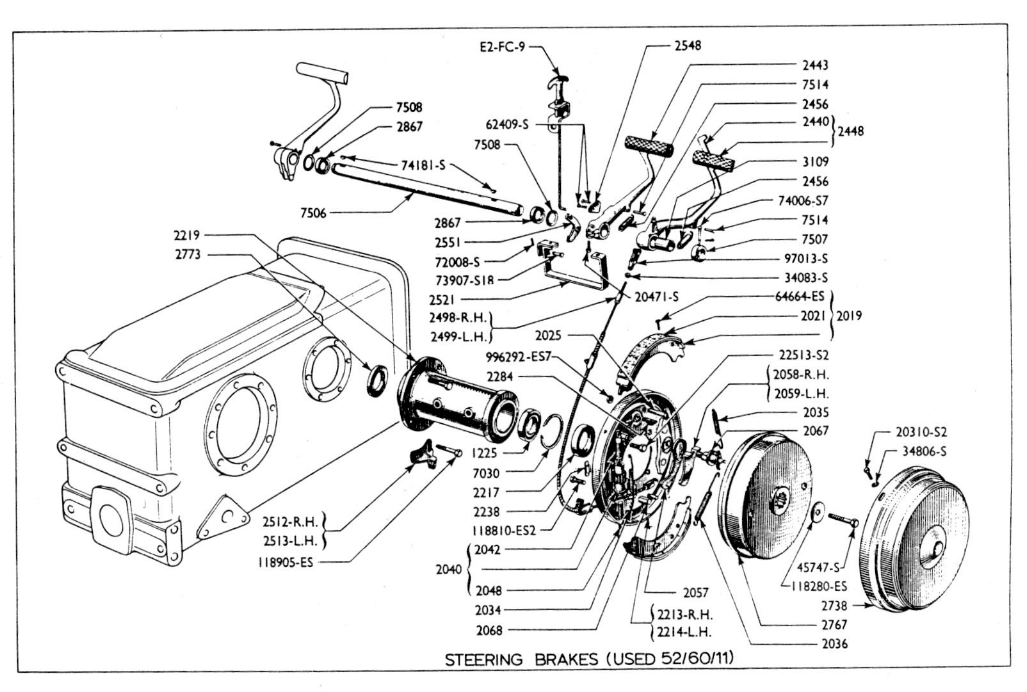

STEERING BRAKES (USED 52/60/11)

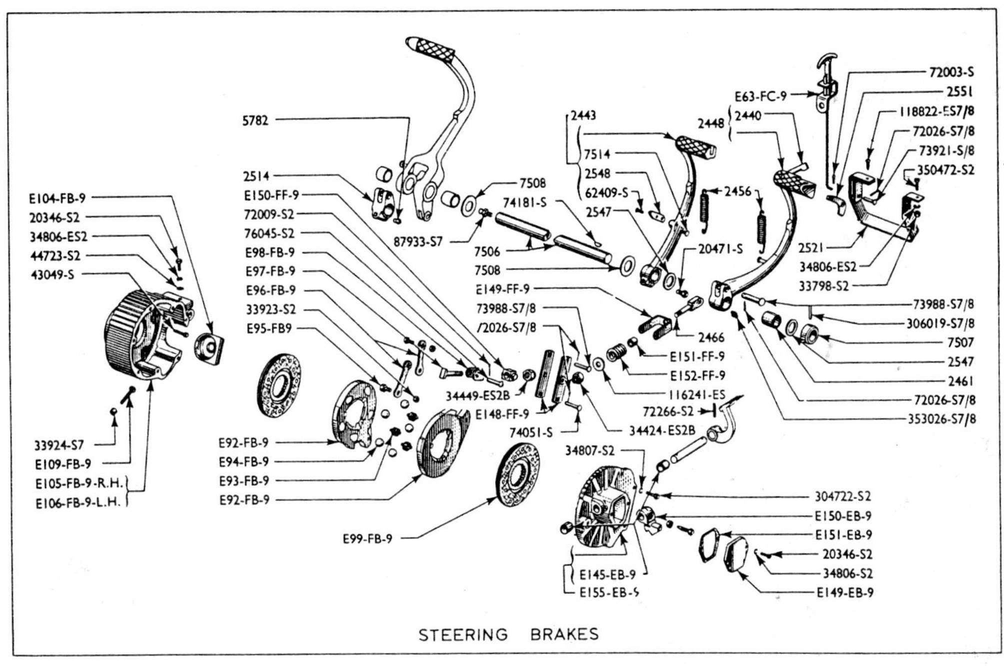

STEERING BRAKES

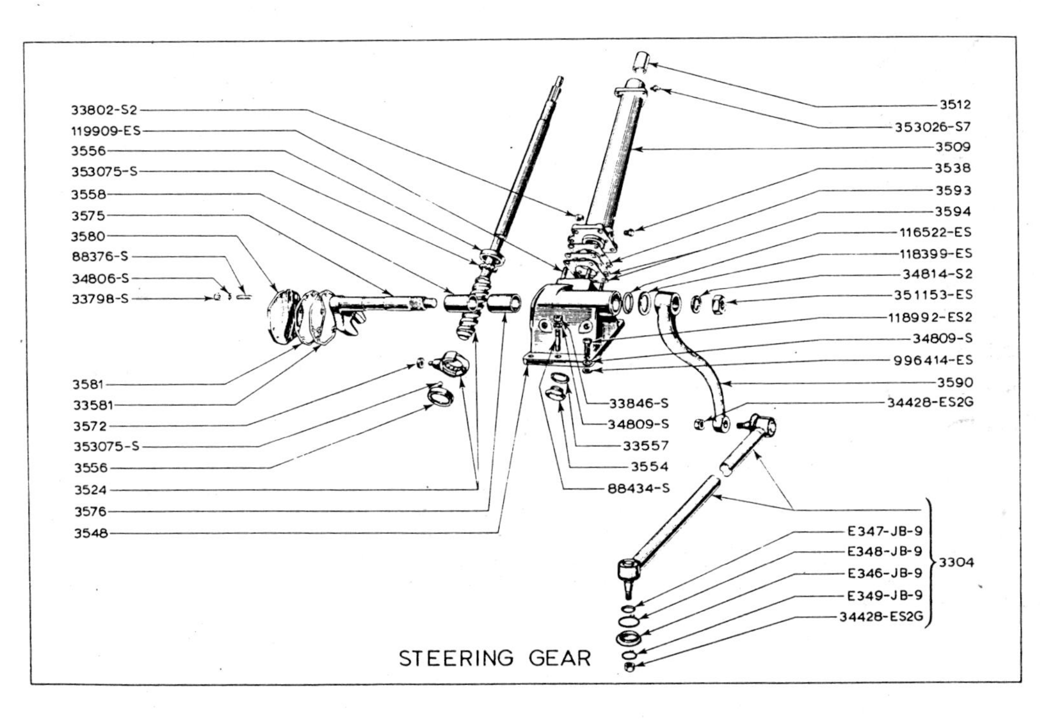

STEERING GEAR

Gearbox & Clutch

The gearbox was based on the 7.7 green spot variant of the E27N but a primary box was fitted in front to give the additional 'high and low' ratios. There was now only one power take off position and that was below, and this gave PTO and hydraulic pump drive. From engine number 1417988 in February 1957 a 'live PTO' was available as an option which incorporated a double clutch assembly. This involved the alteration of the clutch cross shaft which was moved approx. 2" to the rear of the front transmission housing to allow more space for the double clutch. From engine number 1418861 once stocks of the old housing had been used up on 'non live' tractors the new housing was used for all models, resulting in a variation in the parts used for the clutch release mechanism. On 'non live tractors' the primary gear-lever was 'up' for low ratio and 'down' for high ratio; with 'live PTO' the positions were reversed.

The single clutch was 11" diameter, and the dual clutch for 'live' PTO 12" diameter. However a heavy duty single clutch assembly was available from 1952 and was fitted expressly to Muir Hill, Chaseside, and Weatherill units and other skids. A larger diameter 13" clutch was introduced in 1960 and its fitment to any tractor can be noted by the screw cap greaser on the RH side of the front transmission housing. It could be fitted retrospectively to any post 1957 tractor without 'live' PTO. Where a belt pulley and guard was fitted an extension was required to allow the greaser to clear this assembly.

The basic gearbox required alteration to suit the 'live' PTO application, but it was not until the 'New Performance Super Major' that alterations were made to the gearbox which gave revised ratios in all gears, and a better PTO ground speed with increased horsepower at the PTO. (see table).

OVERALL GEAR RATIOS AND ROAD SPEEDS

(Standard Tyres)

Tractors before Serial Number 08C 960337

Gear	RATIOS		1200 R.P.M.		1400 R.P.M.		1700 R.P.M.	
	Gearbox	Overall	M.P.H.	K.P.H.	M.P.H.	K.P.H.	M.P.H.	K.P.H.
1st	6.62	123 : 1	1.56	2.51	1.82	2.92	2.20	3.55
2nd	4.70	87.3 : 1	2.19	3.53	2.56	4.12	3.11	5.00
3rd	3.68	68.4 : 1	2.80	4.50	3.26	5.25	3.96	6.38
4th	2.615	48.6 : 1	3.94	6.34	4.59	7.39	5.58	8.98
5th	1.875	34.8 : 1	5.49	8.84	6.41	10.30	7.79	12.54
6th	1.043	19.3 : 1	9.87	15.90	11.52	18.54	14.05	22.60
H.R.	2.73	50.7 : 1	3.77	6.07	4.40	7.09	5.35	8.60
L.R.	4.91	91.1 : 1	2.10	3.38	2.45	3.94	2.98	4.79

Tractors from Serial Number 08C 960337

4.375 Crown Wheel and Pinion

Gear	RATIOS		1200 R.P.M.		1400 R.P.M.		1700 R.P.M.	
	Gearbox	Overall	M.P.H.	K.P.H.	M.P.H.	K.P.H.	M.P.H.	K.P.H.
1st	7.82	182.00	1.058	1.708	1.235	1.991	1.50	2.42
2nd	6.04	140.20	1.362	2.175	1.588	2.535	1.93	3.08
3rd	4.00	92.88	2.061	3.32	2.405	3.87	2.92	4.70
4th	3.09	71.65	2.67	4.30	3.115	5.01	3.78	6.08
5th	1.875	43.54	4.38	7.06	5.12	8.24	6.22	10.00
6th	0.958	22.25	8.61	13.83	10.02	16.14	12.19	19.60
H.R.	2.96	68.60	2.781	4.475	3.241	5.22	3.94	6.34
L.R.	5.79	134.50	1.425	2.295	1.662	2.678	2.02	3.25

Optional 3.5 to 1 Crown Wheel and Pinion

Gear	RATIOS		1200 R.P.M.		1400 R.P.M.		1700 R.P.M.	
	Gearbox	Overall	M.P.H.	K.P.H.	M.P.H.	K.P.H.	M.P.H.	K.P.H.
1st	7.82	145.60	1.32	2.13	1.54	2.486	1.87	3.02
2nd	6.04	112.10	1.70	2.72	1.985	3.17	2.41	3.85
3rd	4.00	74.30	2.578	4.15	3.008	4.84	3.65	5.87
4th	3.09	57.32	3.338	5.37	3.89	6.26	4.72	7.60
5th	1.875	34.83	5.48	8.83	6.40	10.30	7.77	12.50
6th	0.958	17.80	10.75	17.30	15.54	20.18	15.23	24.50
H.R.	2.96	54.88	3.478	5.58	4.05	6.51	4.92	7.92
L.R.	5.79	107.60	1.778	2.863	2.075	3.34	2.52	4.06

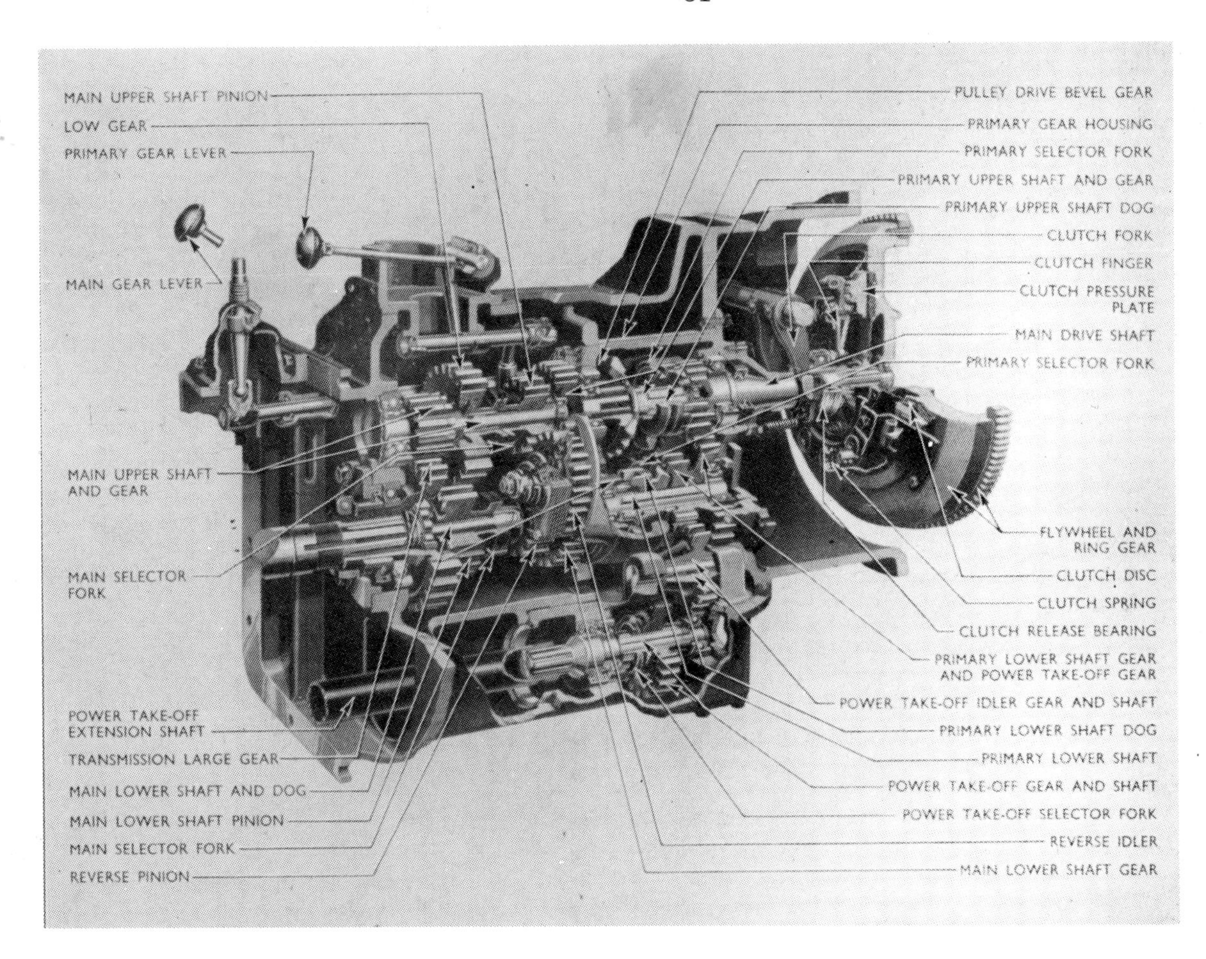

Above: The E1A front transmission showing the gearbox and clutch. The gearbox was based on the old Fordson 7.75 Green Spot assembly with a primary box in front.

Below: With the introduction of a 'live' PTO the gearbox was modified as shown here.

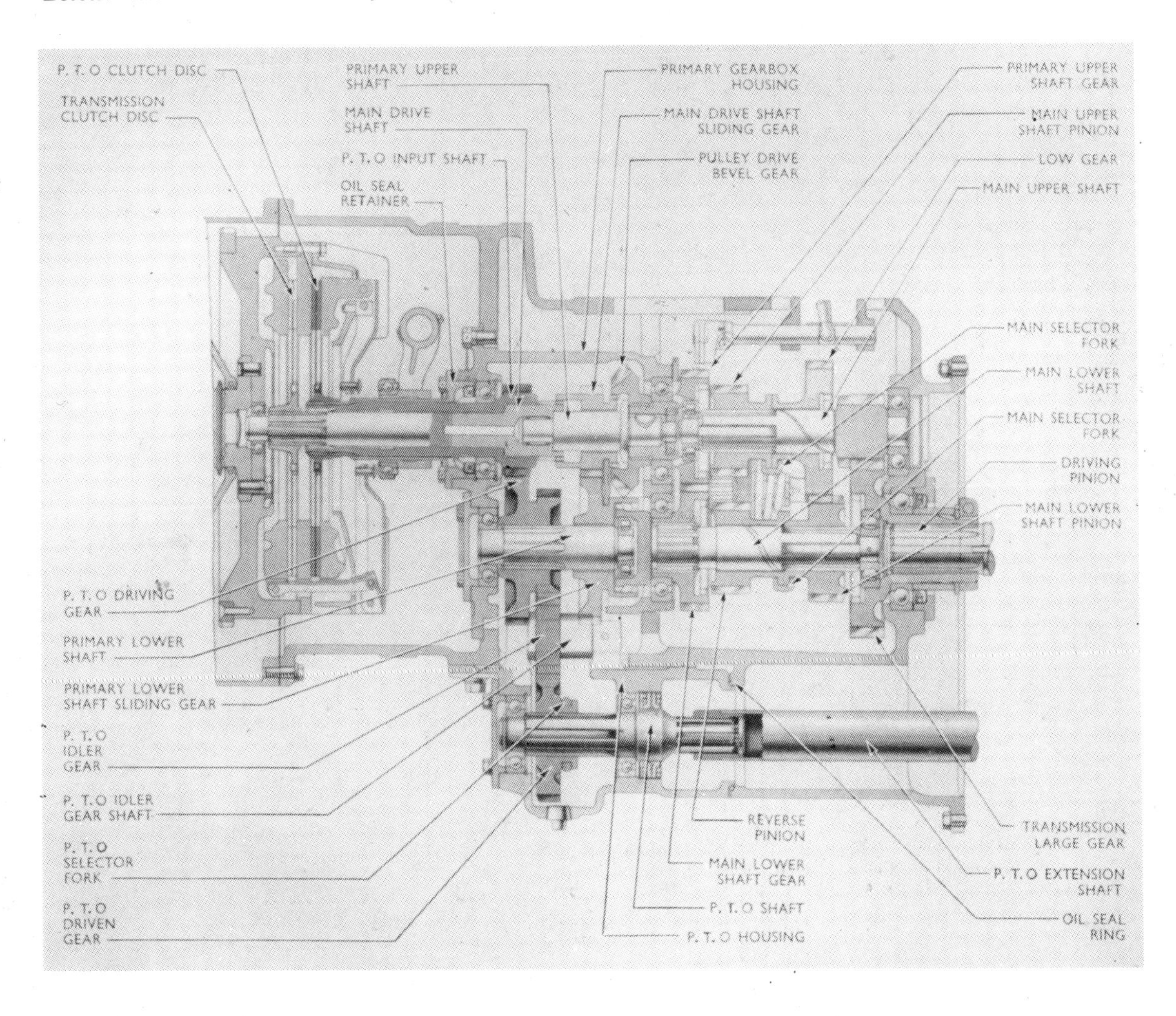

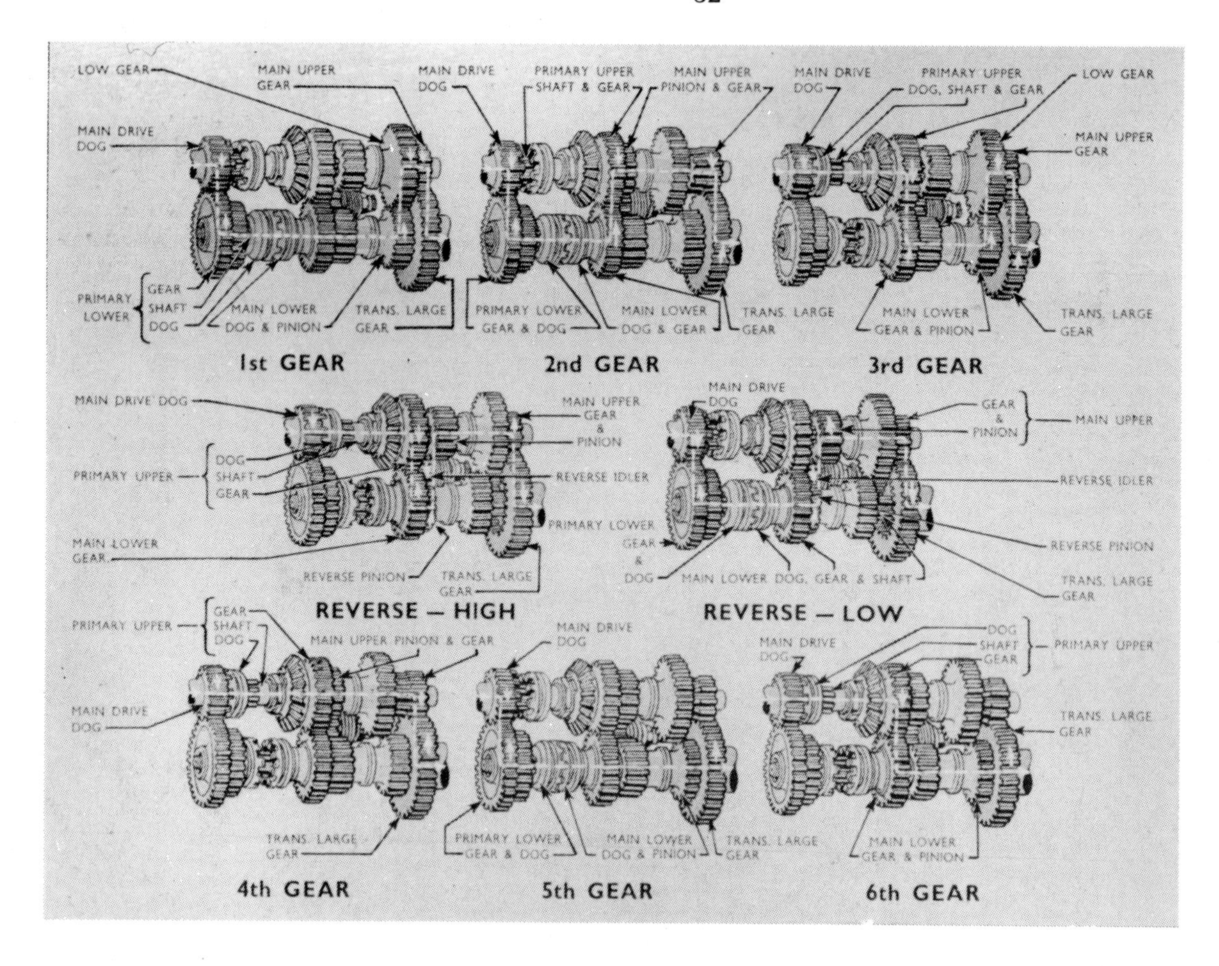

The path which the power took is explained in the diagram above.

The rear transmission was almost entirely E27N (below), but the hydraulic pump was incorporated inside. The design of these components in the form shown dated back to the late 1940s. It had been intended to offer improved hydraulics on the E27N from 1948/9 of identical design but their introduction was deferred until the new model came out.

Opposite Page: Exploded views of the rear axle components until November 1960 (upper), and after (lower).

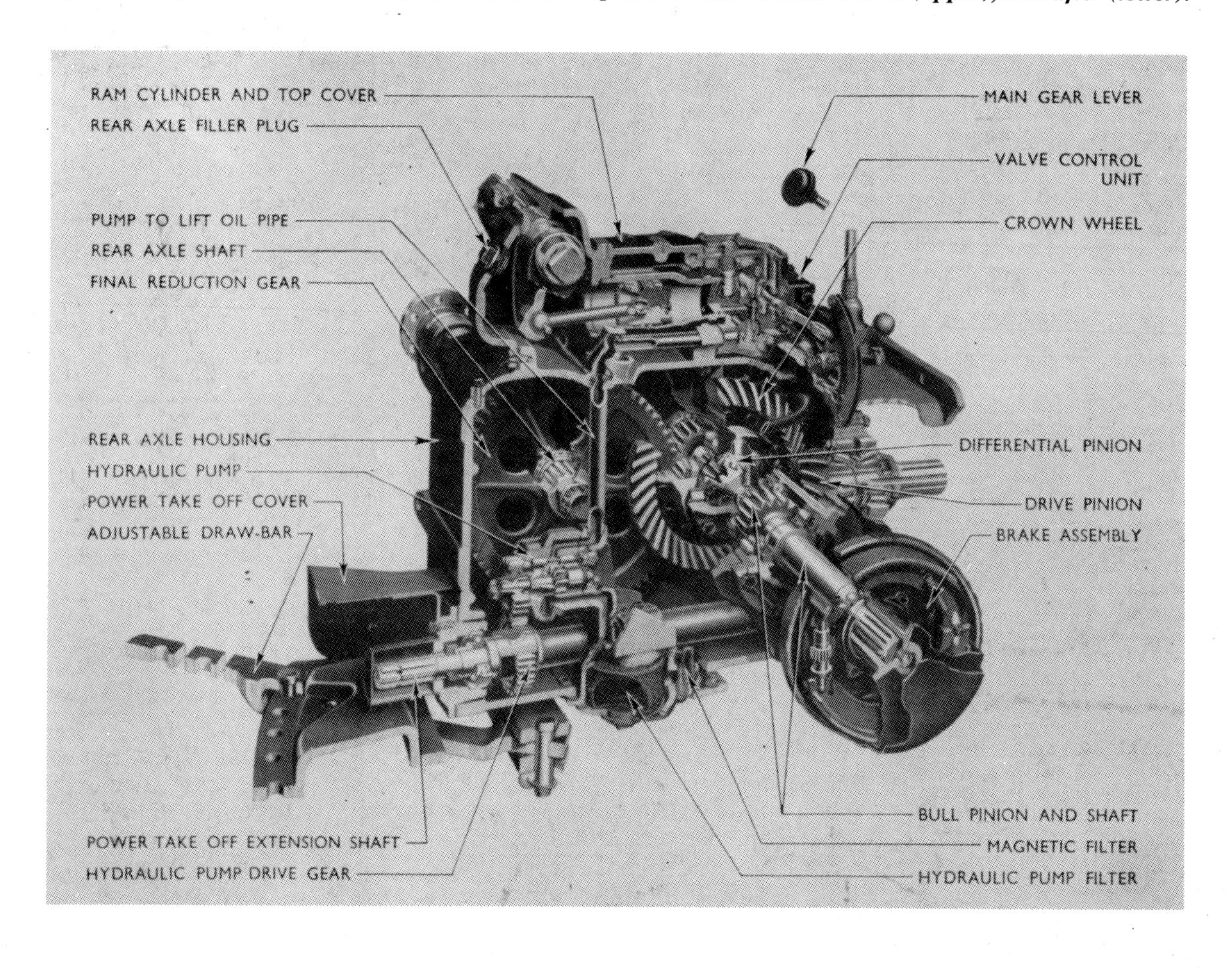

Rear Axle

The rear axle was of course the one item which was inherited almost unchanged from the E27N. There were subtle differences, such as the way in which the gear lever was attached, and the fact that the internals had to be modified to be allow the fitment of the internal hydraulic pump. Two types of rear axle housings were used, those able to take brakes for the Industrial, and the plain ones used on all the other models. When brakes were fitted on Industrial models cone shaped covers bolted over the ends of the bull pinion shafts. With the introduction of the Super Major a differential lock was available. Further changes took place with the Super Major insofar as two crown wheel and pinion ratios of 3.5:1 (the original), and 4.375:1 were available from November 1960, and the final reduction gears were also reduced in diameter at the same date from 17.65" to 17.52".

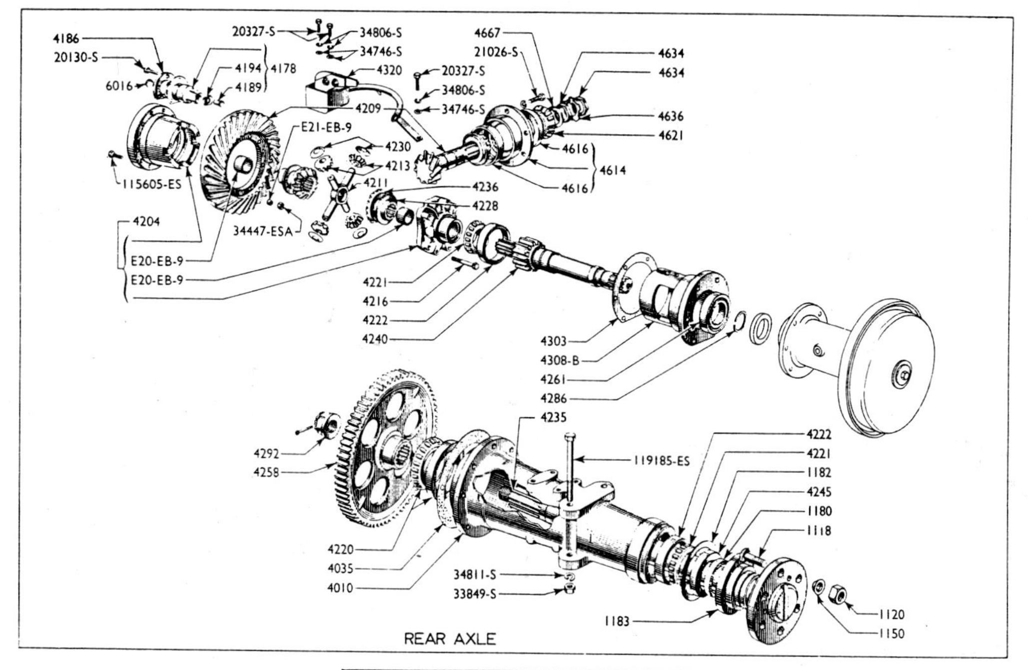

REAR AXLE

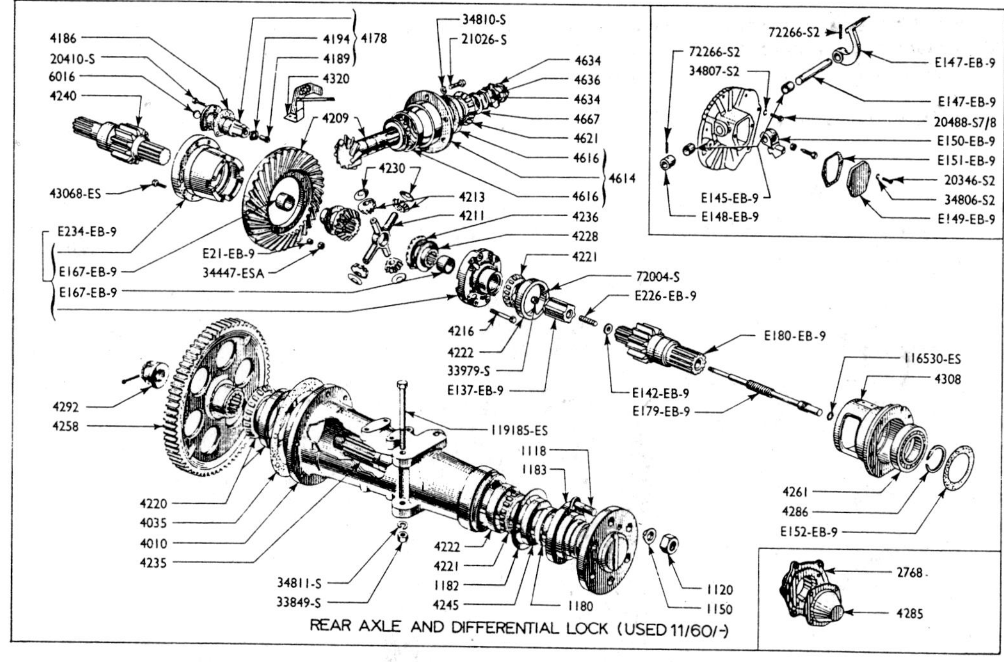

REAR AXLE AND DIFFERENTIAL LOCK (USED 11/60/-)

Drawbar

A much neater drawbar arrangement than the E27N was provided in the form of a steel casting which bolted to the rear corners of the transmission housing and was adjustable for height. A swinging drawbar was provided, and early tractors lacked a clevis on the end of this, which feature was added in 1953.

Industrial tractors had the same drawbar hitch assembly as the E27N.

An Automatic Pick-up hitch was available when a HPL was fitted, and this required the removal of the standard drawbar assembly. The Automatic Hitch was improved with the introduction of the Super Major a design having been evolved which did not interfere with the use of the three point linkage.

Engine

Spark Ignition variants are dealt with first, as the TVO engine ceased production in 1957.

All three engines used many common components, the main difference between the spark ignition and C.I. engines was the cylinder head. VO and Diesel engines were 100mm bore, petrol 97.

Initial VO production (EIADKN) used a separate starting carburettor and automatic changeover to TVO was supposed to take effect when the engine was warmed up and the throttle opened. In practice this unit gave a lot of trouble and was replaced after tractor No. 1239960 with a fixed drain valve type main carburettor which also had a drain-off facility, and a two-way changeover tap beneath the tank. The cylinder head compression ratio was changed from 4.35:1 to 4.62:1 from January 1953, and further modifications to the manifold were made from June 1953. This involved increasing the thickness of the manifold at the engine block to manifold flange, and deleting the manifold drain valve; this was effective from Engine No. 1251122.

Production of VO engined tractors ceased in April 1957, the date when the mark II engine was introduced, whereafter a few petrol engined tractors were built, mainly for export. The throttle linkage on these tractors and VO tractors fitted with replacement cylinder blocks after this date did not operate through the block. The petrol engine remained virtually unaltered until 1964 from 1957, with recalibration of the carburettor being the only main modification with the mark II engine, along with the adoption of new inlet and exhaust manifolds to suit the in-line ports of the cylinder head.

Spark ignition engines could have either a vertical magneto or a distributor with coil ignition. All VO tractors were equipped with radiator shutters, and as these were deleted at tractor 1420356 it can be assumed that it was around this serial that VO engine production ceased.

***Below:* The spark ignition engine in its original form showing the separate starting carburettor used on the E1ADKN (TVO) model but soon discontinued in favour of 'manual' changeover.**
***Bottom:* A sectioned view of the Spark ignition engine.**

Engine (Diesel)

The diesel engine used many common components with the spark ignition version. For ease of reference it has been found necessary to take all engine components together in analysing the changes.

Early diesel engines had the habit of running backwards under certain conditions. The fuel injection pump camshaft was redesigned to prevent this and pumps so modified were stamped 'B'. This took effect from tractor 1239515 (October 1952).

Early Cylinder heads had separate inserts around the injectors, but these were deleted from March 1953 when the injector housings were cast integrally with the head.

Piston ring design was altered around the same time, when the parallel compression rings used in part were eliminated; thereafter all engines used tapered compression rings.

One of the problems with the early diesel engines was a tendency to persistent carboning of exhaust valves and stems. Rotator type exhaust valves were introduced to eliminate this problem, and many engines were retrospectively fitted under warranty. These were fitted in production from approx. engine No. 1257972 (May 1953) and also required shorter exhaust valve guide bushings. Alloy cylinder head bolts were also introduced on diesel and petrol engines in September 1953.

Fram fuel filters came into use in October 1953. In November 1953 the Decompressor lever was eliminated from diesel engines (effective 1269897). It was still available as an extra however.

In December 1953, the fuel injection pump was modified with a cover having eight instead of four bolts. This came into effect from engine 1271510. From April 1954 the injection pump was inclined 10 degrees towards the engine by alteration to the mounting bracket. This involved redesign of injector pipes and other details. The change had nothing to do with tractor design; it was done to suit the fitting of the engine in the new forward control Ford Thames lorry to allow greater clearance next to the driver and prevent the fuel pipes chafing against the bonnet.

Although not fitted as standard, the decompressor control was modified from May 1954 and moved to the front of the rocker cover.

From June 1954, the Excess Fuel and Stop device was modified, from engine No. 1299000, and the engine idling speed was set at 550 rpm from July 1954.

From engine number 1308977 (September 1954) a number of changes were made, including the adoption of a narrow type fan belt with corresponding changes to the crankshaft, generator and water pump pulleys. The timing pointer was no longer fitted to the cylinder front cover, and the flywheel was henceforth marked and accessed by removing the inspection cover on the RH side of the flywheel housing. On diesel tractors it was no longer necessary to fit a starting handle and coupling and the components were deleted.

Piston pin distortion under certain arduous conditions brought about the installation, from engine number 1362380 of solid rather than tubular piston pins, from October 1955.

Injection pump timing was the next matter to receive attention, and this was advanced from 29° to 26° B.T.D.C. in January 1956; this setting could be applied retrospectively to previous engines.

If you were looking for the engine number from tractor 1380939 you would have found that it had been moved from the flywheel housing to the RH. front cylinder block.

Oil filters had previously been bought in from several manufacturers. The Fram type was discontinued in production and only the A.C. and Tecalemit types used, from June 1956, as the latter two types had elements and gaskets which were interchangeable, the Fram type did not and supplies were only available for service thereafter.

For some time Industrial users and converters had expressed the desire for a more powerful engine. A modified inlet manifold derived from the truck one stamped 1800 allowed the engine to develop 44HP @ 1800 rpm with a no load speed of 2050 rpm. This modification was not approved for use on standard agricultural tractors, County Crawlers or Roadless Traction models.

A problem encountered with early engines was leakage of coolant into the sump at the bottom of the liners. To try and eliminate problems in this area, the liner seals were altered from a vee section to a square section in February 1957, from engine number 1416677.

The Mark II Engine

With the elimination of the TVO model, a sump with inspection cover was no longer serviced; taking effect from April 1957. This heralded the most important changes to the engine since production started. From 4th April, engine number 1425097 the following modifications were effected:-

The first item to be modified were the manifolds, which now had in-line instead of staggered ports. On the early engines the throttle linkage had passed through the cylinder block, but on the new block there was no provision for this, the throttle linkage having been redirected via the rear of the block.

The rocker shafts were modified and the rocker cover was now retained by six screws around the outer flange instead of two central screws on the top. A new steel cylinder head gasket replaced the previous copper asbestos type and of course the porting changes required new cylinder heads. The cylinder block was modified in various ways, with two tapped holes provided at the rear to carry the rear throttle linkage, breathing and oil circulation improved. The oil pump cover now incorporated the oil relief valve, and in consequence a deeper sump was fitted. The camshaft fitted was now common to all 4 cylinder engines, petrol and diesel, truck and tractor. Changes in the ventilation system for the crankcase produced a new timing cover.

The pistons were modified by moving the combustion chambers and fitting thicker piston pins, whilst crankshaft, main bearings, cylinder liners and seals remained the same as before. Injectors had larger spray holes, and changes to the injection pump to allow for greater engine power, by increasing the plungers and barrels from 7.0mm to 7.5mm caused the timing to be set at 22° BTDC.

The above changes were not heavily publicised, as they were part of the improvement programme to the tractor culminating in the introduction of the Power Major.

A high speed manifold for the latest type of engine was also released but was not approved for use on agricultural tractors.

Above: The diesel engine in section.

Left: The original format of diesel engine with vertical injection pump, and decompressor lever to the rear of the cylinder head.

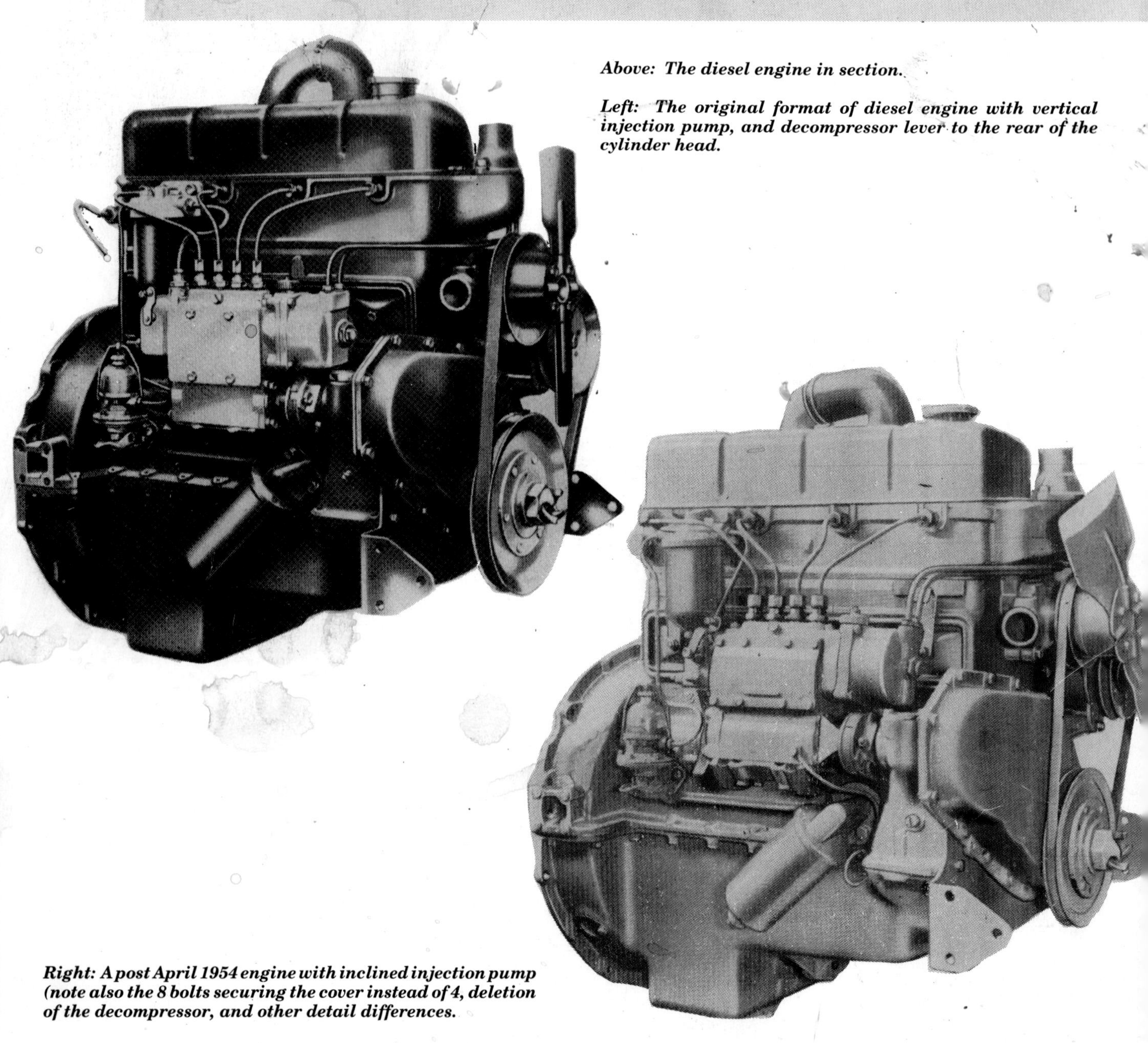

***Right:** A post April 1954 engine with inclined injection pump (note also the 8 bolts securing the cover instead of 4, deletion of the decompressor, and other detail differences.*

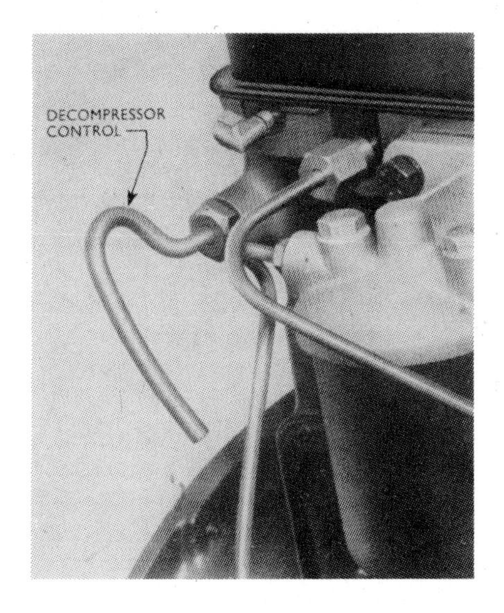

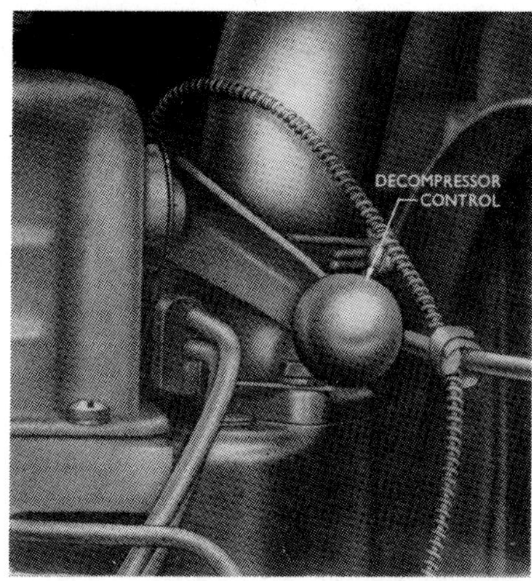

Above: ***The original decompressor control mounted on the rear of the cylinder head.***

Above Right: ***From May 1954 the decompressor, when fitted as an option, was operated by a lever at the front of the rocker cover.***

Right: ***The inertia starter available as an option for export tractors to allow the elimination of any electrical equipment.***

Below: ***Fuel system layouts, the upper with the original Simms pump with pneumatic governor, and the lower with Simms 'Minimec' pump fitted from May 1962. Some early Spanish built (Ebro) tractors in 1965/6 used the original type of pump for an unknown reason.***

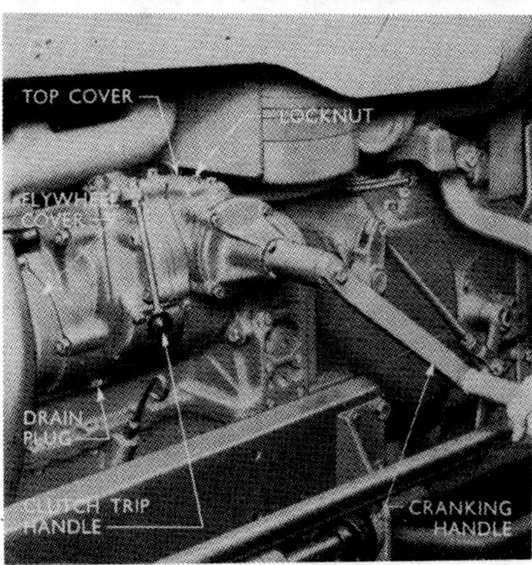

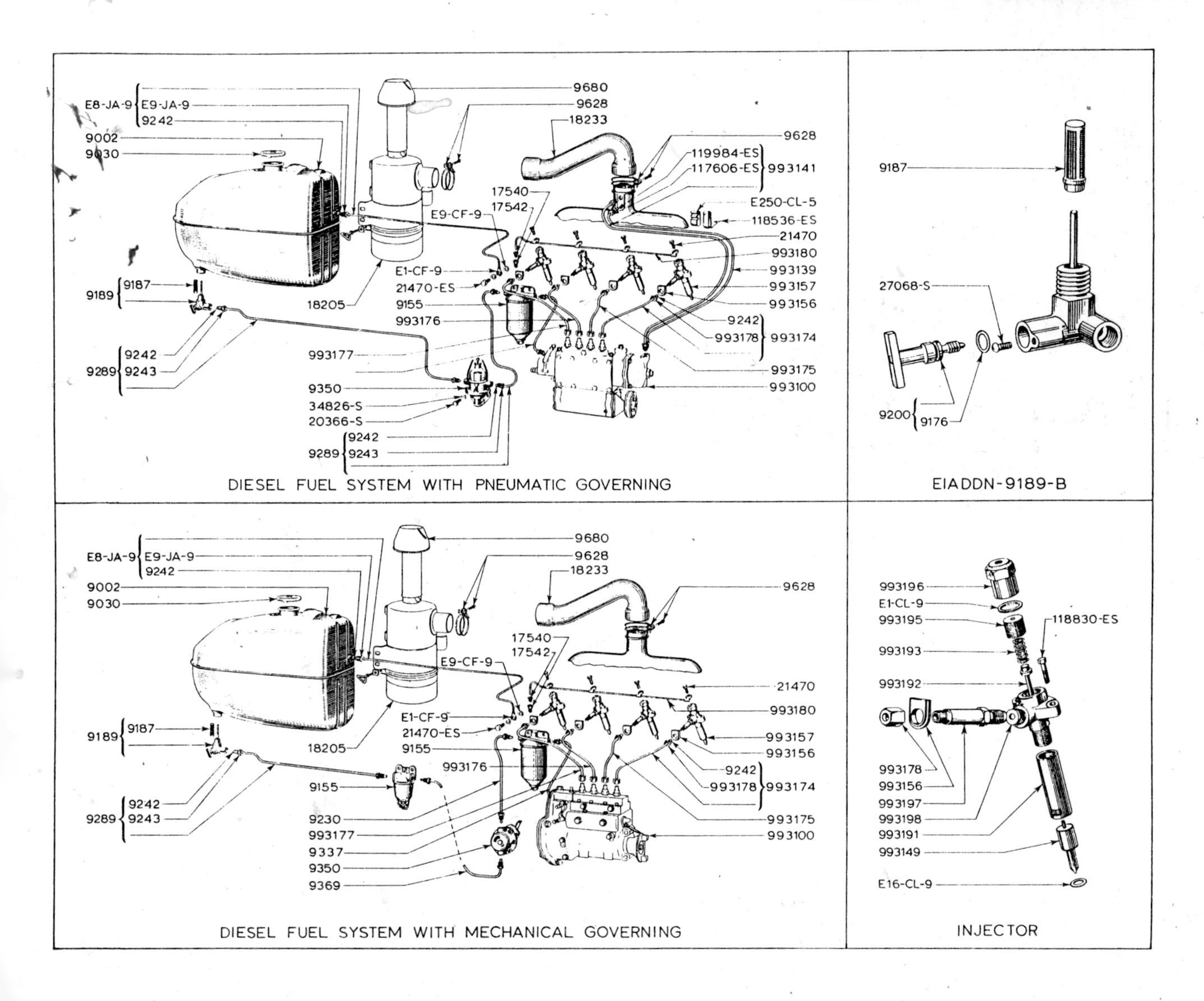

The Power Major

The introduction of the Power Major in July 1958 heralded further detail changes to the engine. Firstly, the 51.8 BHP power output at 1600 RPM brought the tractor into the 'over 50HP' range for the first time.

To achieve the additional 7BHP modifications were made to the valve rockers to increase volumetric efficiency, and the plunger stroke on the fuel injection pump was increased to give a faster injection rate. Combined with truck type delivery valves in the pump and a return to the original type of injectors this gave the necessary increase in fuel delivery to attain the increased power output.

The extra power output of the engines did not arrive without problems, and after a few crankshaft failures, the fillet radii between the crankshaft webs and journals was increased necessitating narrower connecting rod and main bearing liners. This took effect from engine 1483140 in September 1958.

The inevitable head gasket problems still occurred from time to time and from engine 1518654 a new type using copper faced with interleaves of Permanite and Rubber/Asbestos was introduced in July 1959.

If you drove a Power Major built before No. 1539941 you would notice that the throttle lever was set at a different angle. This was because in January 1960 the detail assembly of the throttle linkage was modified and the location of the control lever moved 15° clockwise to make operation easier.

More liner and head gasket modifications were made from August 1960 with the introduction of a composition type head gasket and a change to the top face of the liners to match the new design of gasket. Tractor 1565580 was the first so fitted.

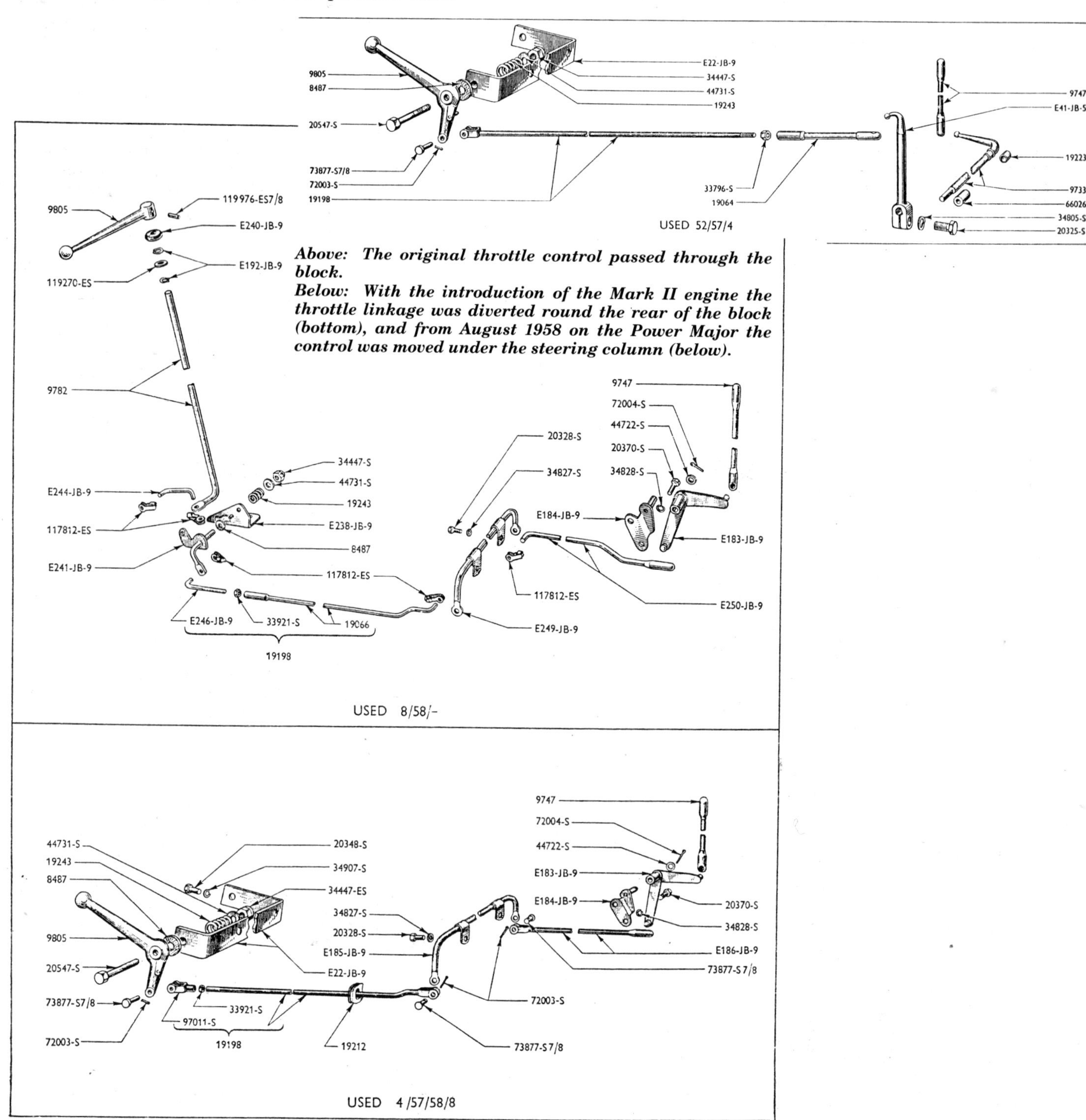

Above: ***The original throttle control passed through the block.***
Below: ***With the introduction of the Mark II engine the throttle linkage was diverted round the rear of the block (bottom), and from August 1958 on the Power Major the control was moved under the steering column (below).***

The Super Major

This was phased in between October and November 1960 but it was March 1961 before any real changes were made to the engine, from engine 1594009. Cylinder liners were given a greater wall thickness, an additional sealing ring added between the upper cylinder block and liner, along with new cylinder block and main bearing bolts. New exhaust valves were also introduced, which were actually manufactured in two pieces.

More changes came later in 1961, with the fitting of timing gears of increased width, which of course necessitated a modified camshaft, new engine front mounting plate, a modified fuel injection pump coupling, all from engine 1599502 and heavier valve springs were added later.

In order to facilitate the introduction of computer technology to aid production, engine numbering was altered from November 1961. The prefix and suffix letters and numbers added enabled each model to be identified by the Computer. Readers should refer to the list of monthly serial numbers for further details.

From serial 08B-756398 (May 1962) the Simms "Minimec" fuel injection pump was introduced in production. This was a unit with integral mechanical governor which provided for more precise engine governing. This more compact unit also required the redesign of the fuel lift pump and a separate filter was provided. The '1800' RPM engine was also available as an option for industrial units required a pump modified inasmuch as it had a different governor spring, delivery valve assemblies, and different calibration. The no load speed of this engine was set at 2020 RPM, whilst the standard engine was set at 1825 RPM.

In July 1963 the New Performance Super Major was introduced, and the extra power available was obtained by altering the injection pump settings so that the 'no load' speed was 1925 RPM. This gave an increase in power output from 51.8BHP to 53.7BHP.

The Spanish built Ebro Super 55 and its successors retained the final design of engine used until the end of Dagenham production in October 1964.

Below Left: The carburettor used on Petrol and TVO tractors was an adaptation of the same unit used on 'N' and 'E27N' tractors from 1939 on but a fixed jet was fitted from October 1952.

Below Right: The exhaust and inlet manifolds on all but the TVO tractor were separate units; the drawings show manifolds for the Mark I engine with staggered ports., the bottom unit being for a petrol tractor.

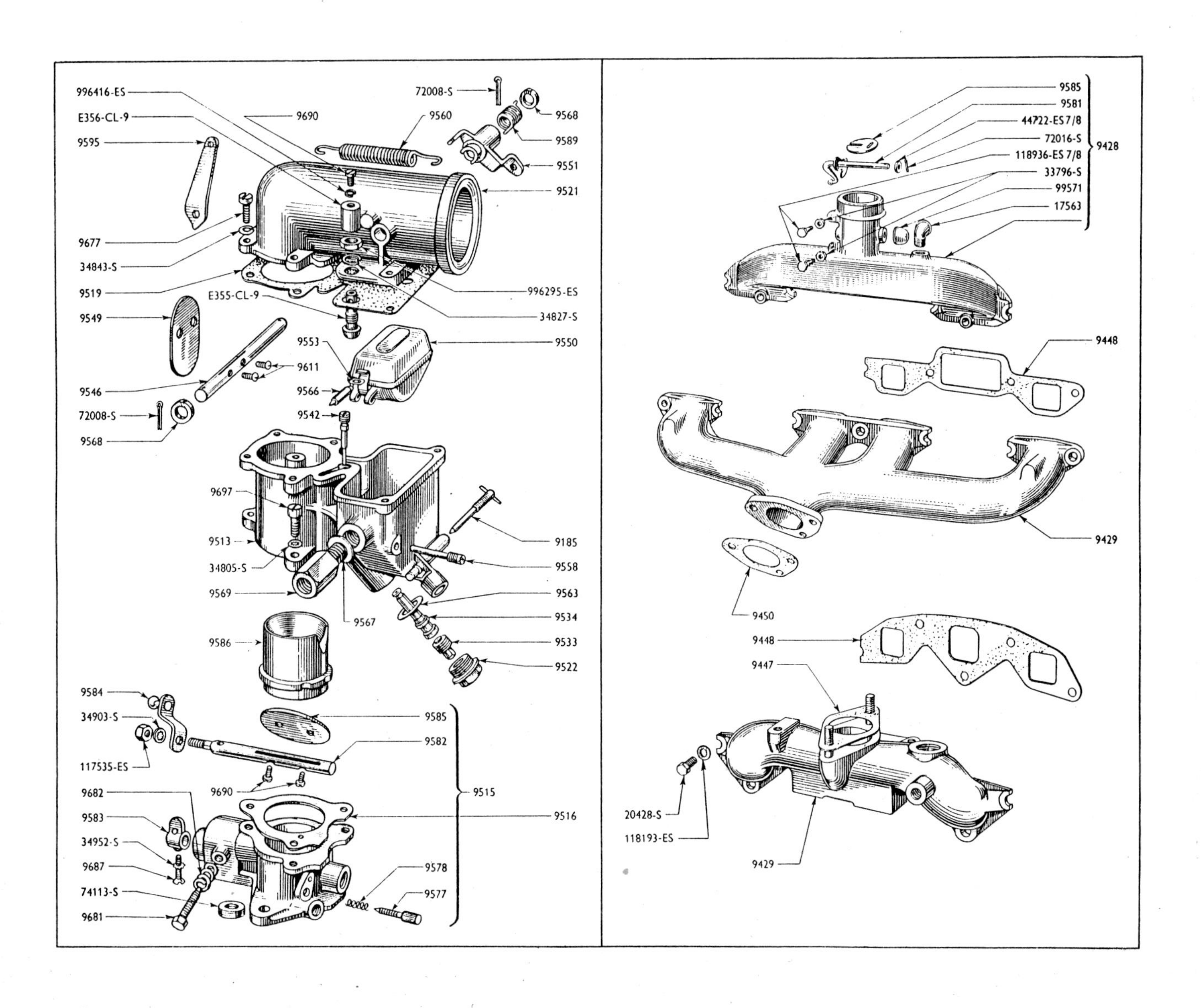

Cooling System

The New Major represented a departure from previous Fordson tractors in that the Radiator was not part of the tractor structure, but was purely functional, being enclosed in the tractor front cowl. The original radiator assembly had a built in filler neck and consisted of 10 fins per inch. Thermostat setting was From January 1955 a separate filler neck was provided, and from March 1957, engine number 1420356, diesel tractors were fitted with a core having 5 fins per inch. Radiator shutters were deleted from all models, and thermostats set to 190°F. Until March 1958 two bladed fans, 18" in diameter for the VO and petrol engines, and 15" diameter for the diesel were fitted, with an option of four blades for tropical use on petrol and VO tractors. From March 1958 the assemblies were changed in design but with the introduction of the Power Major in August 1958, the truck type radiator filler cap was adopted along with a 17" 2 blade fan , again with an option of 4 blades for export. In February 1961, from engine number 1571825 the diameter was again increased to 18". The method of mounting the radiator was changed from tractor 08B-767403 in September 1962, and this necessitated a new design of crossmember. When fitting the new radiator to previous design tractors an adaptor kit was provided. The cooling system was originally pressurised on all models, but from May 1954 the pressure cap installation was made optional, expressly for export territories.

Air Cleaners

A similar cylindrical aircleaner to the E27N was used on the New Major, and supplies were again purchased from two companies, AC and Burgess. On early tractors until 1954 the primary cleaner was normally located under the bonnet, with the option of a vertical position for export or crawler applications. From 1954 the primary aircleaner protruded through the bonnet. This was a dome shaped unit. With the introduction of the Mark II engine in 1957 a cone shaped pre-cleaner was adopted to allow for increased air volume, although some of this type of pre-cleaner were used previously. The aircleaner unit itself was modified after engine 1425097 to allow for a connection to the rocker cover as part of the engine ventilation system, and further modifications were made for both the Power and Super Major tractors, these being hardly discernable externally. Such alterations as were made were most likely to have been due to an upgrading of specification by the supplier, as by the mid 1950s both Burgess and AC supplied what was in effect a standard range of oilbath cleaners with mountings altered to suit the application.

Aircleaners: these are both the post 1954 design, although the domed pre-cleaner was used on diesel tractors until 1957.

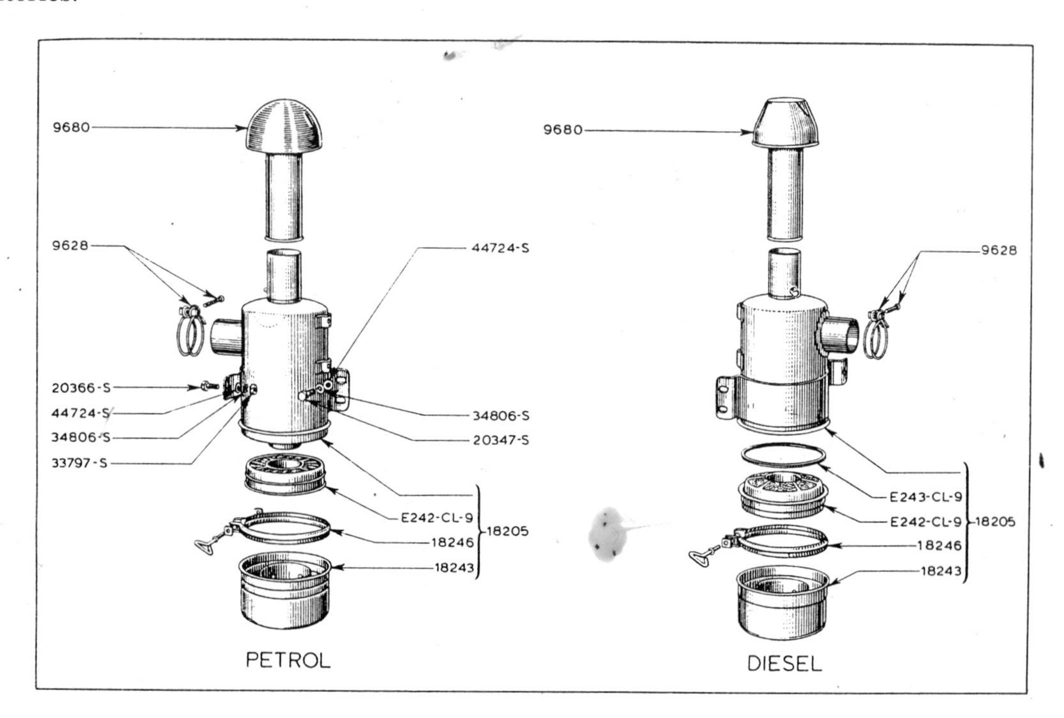

Exhaust System

The original specification of the New Major provided for a horizontal exhaust system, which along with the lack of an external aircleaner gave the tractor very clean lines. As with the pre 1936 Fordson 'N' the underswept system was none too popular with drivers so the option of a vertical exhaust was available. The original vertical silencer was of the 'sausage' design as used on the E27N but with internal baffles. From April 1957 a new design of Burgess silencer with flat ends (the top end was in fact slightly coned) and greater external diameter was adopted at the time of the Mark II engine, and this lasted until the advent of the Super Major when the design was altered slightly; the plain pipe at the top being rather longer. County Crawler tractors were initially fitted with the 'sausage' pattern having a much longer top pipe, and a pre-cleaner extension was also available for this model, which strangely found its way onto the Ebro Super 55! For applications where a loader was fitted, a special exhaust elbow could be fitted to the manifold which required the vertical silencer to pass through the bonnet.

Electrical System

A 12 volt electrical system was fitted, and this of course was designed to be an integral part of the tractor as opposed to previous models where it was an addition. The starter and dynamo locations need no comment as they followed the usual automotive practice, but the battery was neatly located under the bonnet in front of the fuel tank. The starter on the Petrol and TVO models was of the standard type, but the diesel tractor had manual engagement of the starter dog by means of a lever which also actuated the starter solenoid.

Headlamps and side/tail lamps were available as extra equipment. Original equipment consisted of headlamps mounted on the side of the radiator cowl, side lamps mounted on the front of the mudguard tops, and a single rear lamp/number plate illuminator. New lighting regulations from 1954 required the fitting of twin rear lamps incorporating reflectors and these were attached to posts bolted to the rear of the mudguard tops.

An alternative position for the headlamps was provided from tractor number 1456550 for use when the belt to driven equipment from the drive pulley fouled the normal position.

The Super Major saw relocation of the headlamps in the front grilles on tractors for domestic sale, although those for some export territories continued to have the headlamps mounted on the outside of the radiator cowling.

From 1956 two six volt batteries were fitted instead of one twelve volt unit on diesel tractors. A 12 volt unit of less capacity was fitted to VO and petrol units throughout production.

The instrument panel on New Major tractors was fitted below the fuel tank, and incorporated an ignition/lighting switch with key, ammeter, and temperature gauge. On Petrol and VO tractors this panel also incorporated the starter switch and choke control; on diesels the engine stop control. The Power Major and subsequent models had an instrument panel mounted under the steering column on top of the fuel tank; only the lighting switch and engine stop control (diesel)/choke and starter control (petrol) were fitted in a modified housing below.

For export territories a hand operated inertia starter was available.

Petrol and VO tractors had coil ignition as standard with the distributor mounted vertically on the front RH side of the engine. A Lucas 4VRA Magneto was available as an option.

A ploughing light was available as an accessory and mounted on the RH mudguard rear.

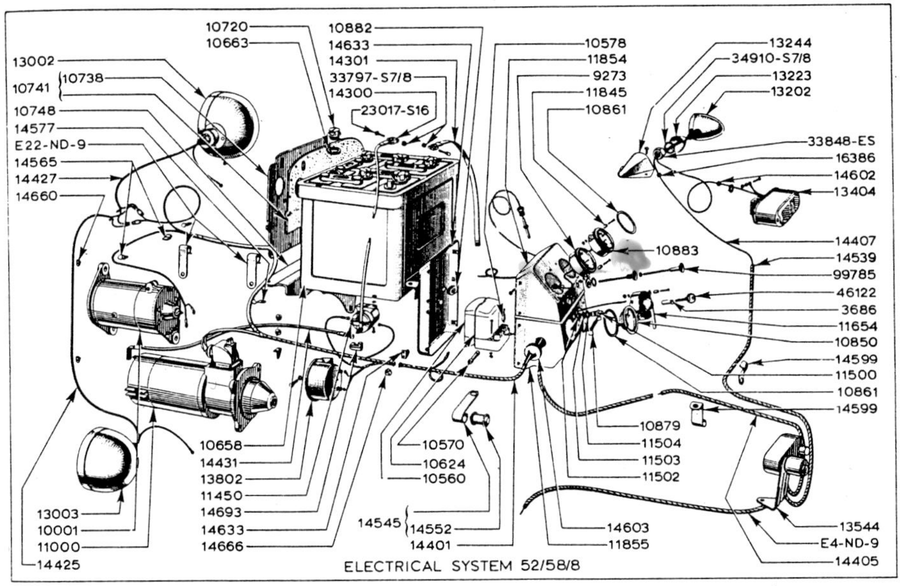

Details of electrical equipment. Two six volt batteries were used on post 1956 tractors however.

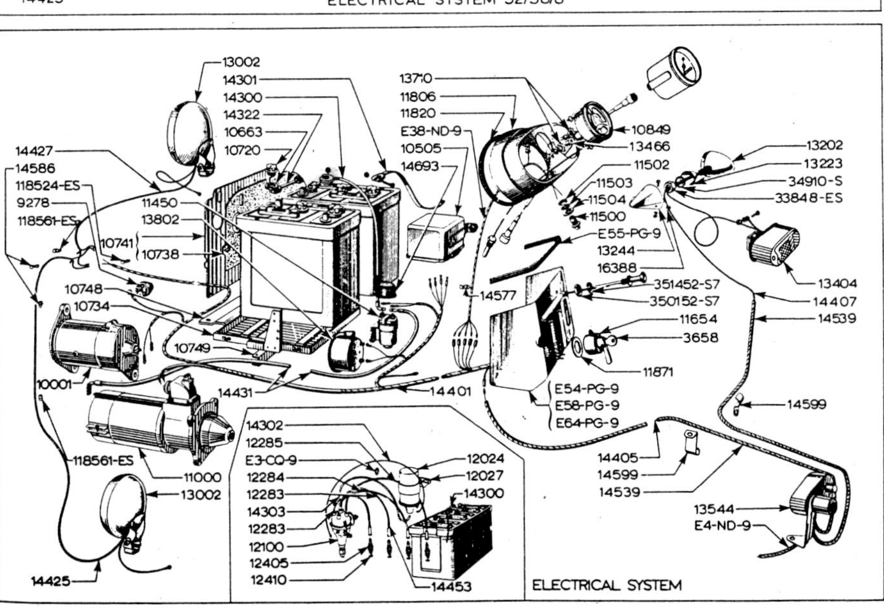

Mudguards & Tinwork

The pre-production and early production tractors had a distinctive style of mudguard of which there were two styles. The original concept of the 'one piece pressing' as envisaged for the E27N but not proceeded with because of tooling costs was taken up with the E1A models. It would appear that the first style incorporated only one curved rib on the inside of the wings at the point where the side and top converged; for added strength and to prevent drumming two horizontal ribs were soon added. The final design which lasted throughout production featured three horizontal ribs. The New Major had footplates which folded up and over the bull pinion extensions, the Power Major had shorter footplates which stopped short of these, and the Super Major had modified wings with footplates profiled to clear the disc brake assemblies.

The same style of bonnet and radiator cowl was used throughout production, with detail changes to suit aircleaner and headlamp positions. Front grille panels were originally woven wire, later pressed mesh, and were of course altered for the Super Major to take the headlamps. Export and special application Super Majors had grille panels with three reinforcement pressings, where headlamps were mounted externally.

Decals & Badges

The 'wheatsheaf' badge in the form of an enamelled die-casting was fitted to the front cowl of all Fordson and Power Major models. The words 'Super Major' were added on either side from November 1960. Although an 'industrial' emblem had been designed in similar style to the 'wheatsheaf' badge it is not certain whether these were actually used in production, certainly the 'commercial' demonstration tractors featured this badge.

Bonnet badges started with a simple

FORDSON
MAJOR.

from 1952.

Later the word **DIESEL** was added below on diesel engined tractors.

From 1954 diesel engined tractors had the

D FORDSON
MAJOR
IESEL.

logo. The Power and Super Majors also had die-cast badges until the advent of the New performance model which had stick on decals. For US export, this model was called the Ford Diesel 5000. A triangular 'live' sticker was affixed to the lower rear bonnet sides of Super Majors but was deleted from December 1962 as being considered unnecessary. New Fordson Majors and Power Majors had a 'live' badge attached to the RH radiator grille panel. The original Ebro Super 55 had badges die cast to suit the front radiator panel, and bonnet sides, later models with the MF tinwork followed the convention of the MF '100' series before moving away to a completely new style.

Below: Details of cooling system, and tinwork until 1960.

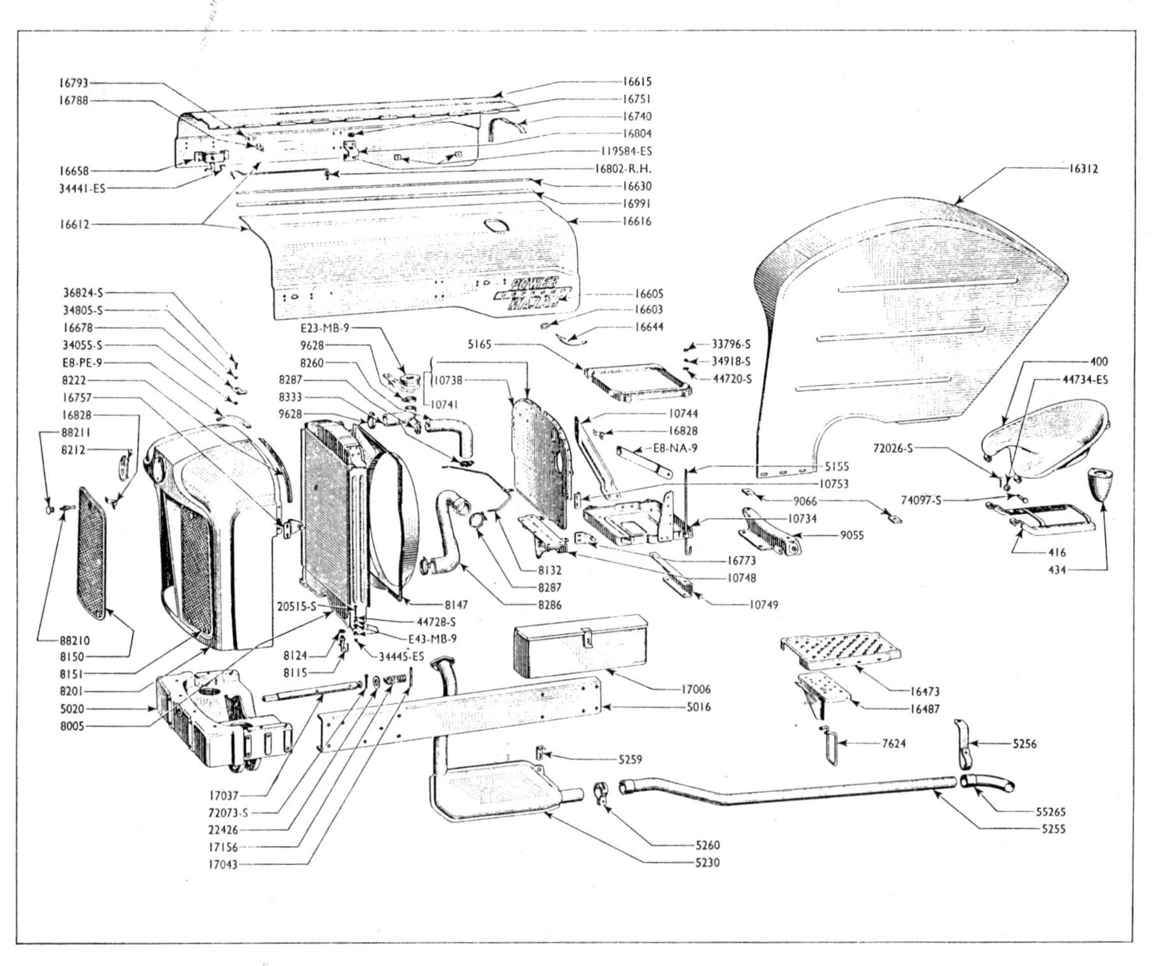

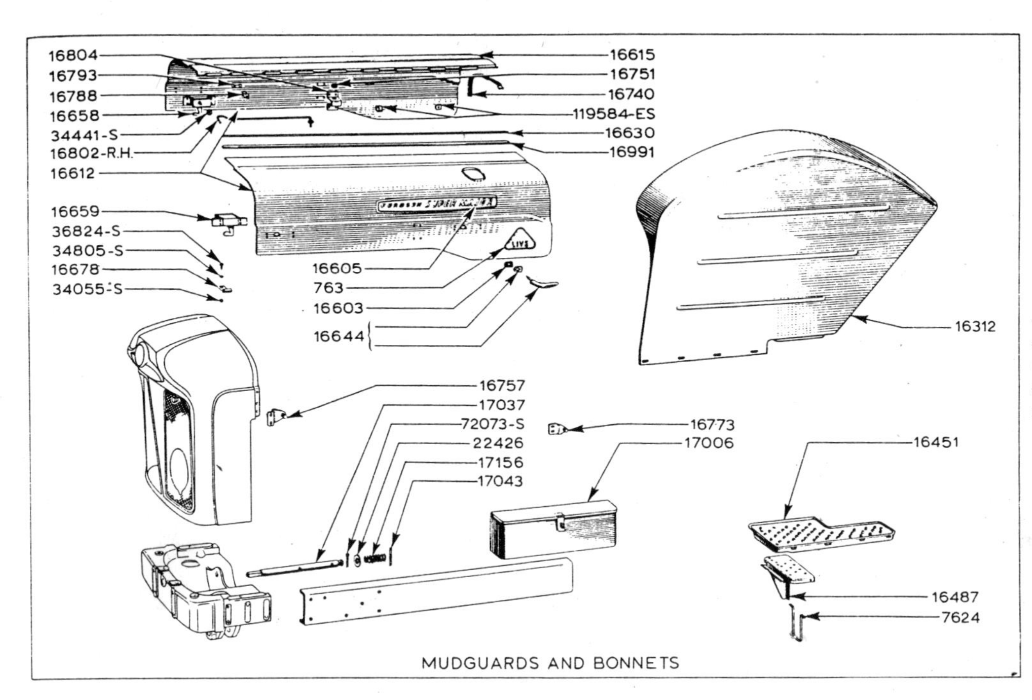

Left: Tinwork on the Super Major; note the higher footboards and no need for cut-outs to clear the brakes on the mudguards.

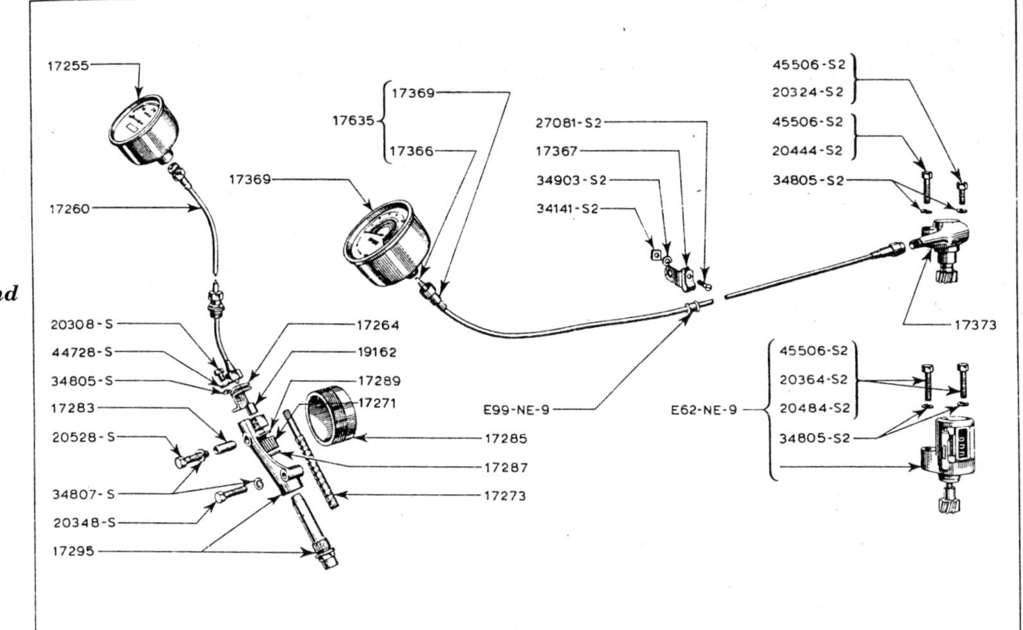

Right: The Proofmeter and hourmeter installations.

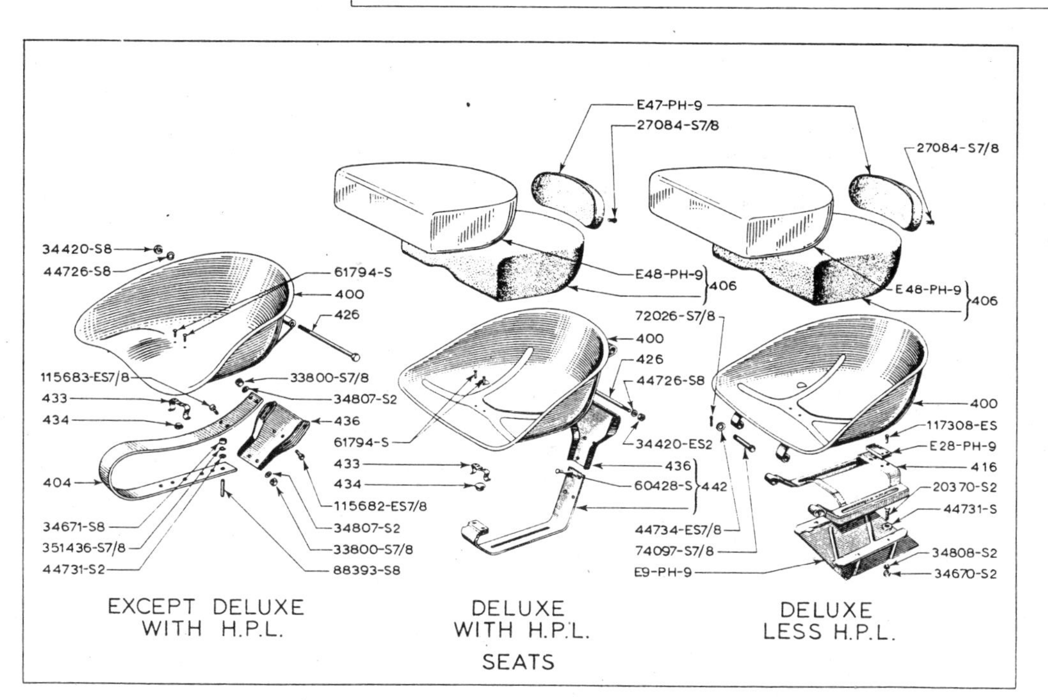

Left: Seats.

Accessories - Hydraulic Power Lifts

The original HPL assembly for the New Major was based on the Smith design for the E27N but with the hydraulic pump installed inside the rear transmission. The rear transmission oil was used and there was no pump and drive at the front. Control was now by a quadrant on the RH side of the assembly. Linkage was inherited from the E27N. Tractors were of course available without hydraulics, including the industrial model; this model which was more commonly known as the 'commercial' tractor could have hydraulics but required the fitting of the standard drawbar assembly to be completely successful.

The first stage in giving more control came when 'preset' linkage became an accessory in 1955, to allow use with the Ransomes TS73 plough which did not have a depth wheel. A cam fitted to the RH lift arm and a manual control lever was used to control depth, in conjunction with a telescopic top link. The top link could be locked in position for use under normal circumstances.

Apart from the redesign of the unloader valve the hydraulics continued almost unchanged in the Power Major period. A single Auxiliary Service valve was available which bolted alongside the existing control quadrant.

The Ferguson System patents having expired and hydraulics with depth control having been used on the 1958 Dexta, this facility was extended to the Super Major. The automatic draft control only operated in compression on the top link. The New Performance Super Major operated with the top link in either compression or tension. The main difference between Super Major and New Performance Super Major units was the provision of a drop control valve on the latter. An improved hydraulic pump was incorporated in the rear transmission and relied on the oil supply from there. Position control/Qualitrol was activated by a separate lever.

The automatic hydraulic clutch release was available as an option on all models, the installation having been modified to take account of the 'live PTO' and sensing top link of the later models. A Dual Auxiliary Service Valve was available for the Super Major, this mounted on the LH side of the tractor between the mudguard and the HPL housing.

Power Take Offs.

The standard central PTO giving the standard speed of 542 RPM @ 1200 RPM of engine rotation was fitted, also driving the hydraulic pump. A raised PTO was available as an option. The belt pulley drive fitted instead of a plate on the RH front transmission housing and was virtually identical to the unit used on 'N' and 'E27N' tractors. With the bevel drive gear being inside the primary gearbox however, two running speeds were obtainable; 779 RPM or 1400 RPM.

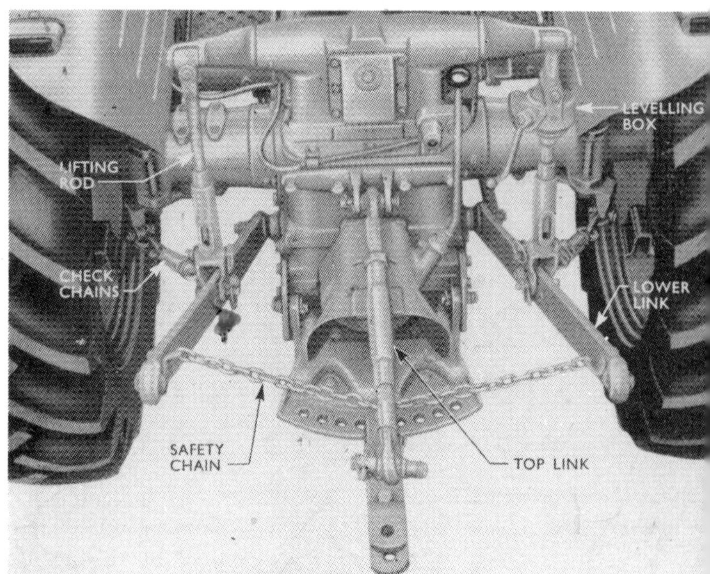

Above Right and below: The original Hydraulic Power Lift and linkage installation.

Below Right: The pre-set linkage control for use with the Ransomes TS73 plough.

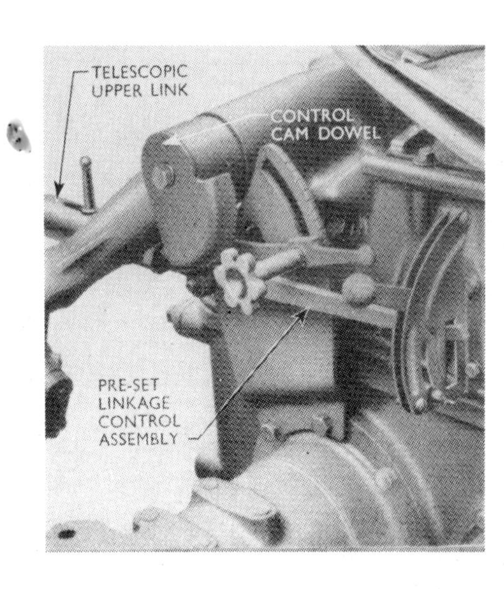

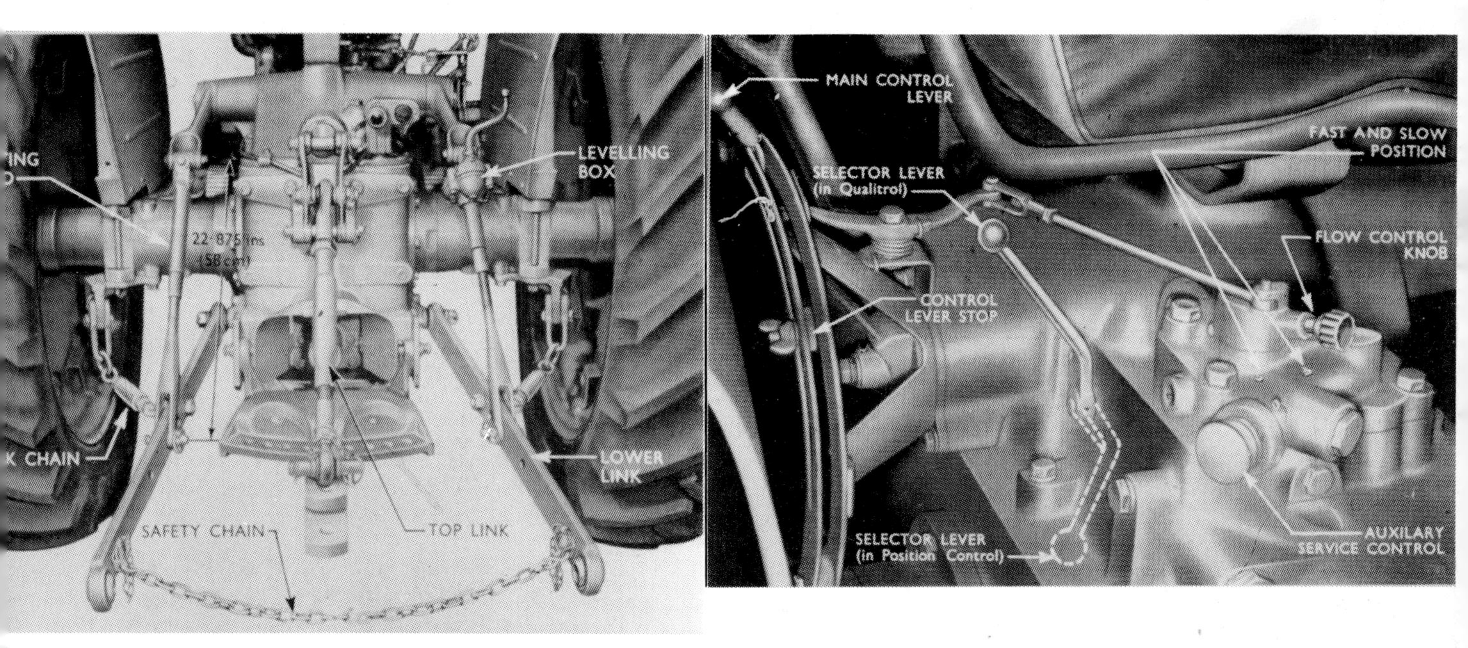

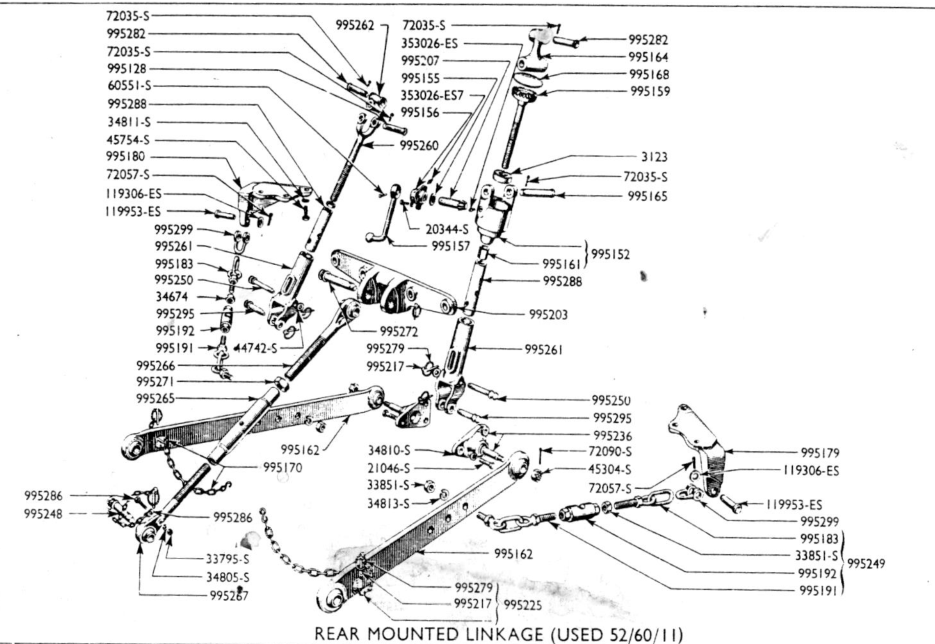

Above Left: The hydraulic lift with draft control introduced on the Super Major.

Above Right: The Super Major controls, showing the Position control/ Qualitrol lever.

Left: Exploded views of the linkage.

Bottom: The draft control installation as applied to the Super Major. It was possible to offer this facility due to expiration of Ferguson patents.

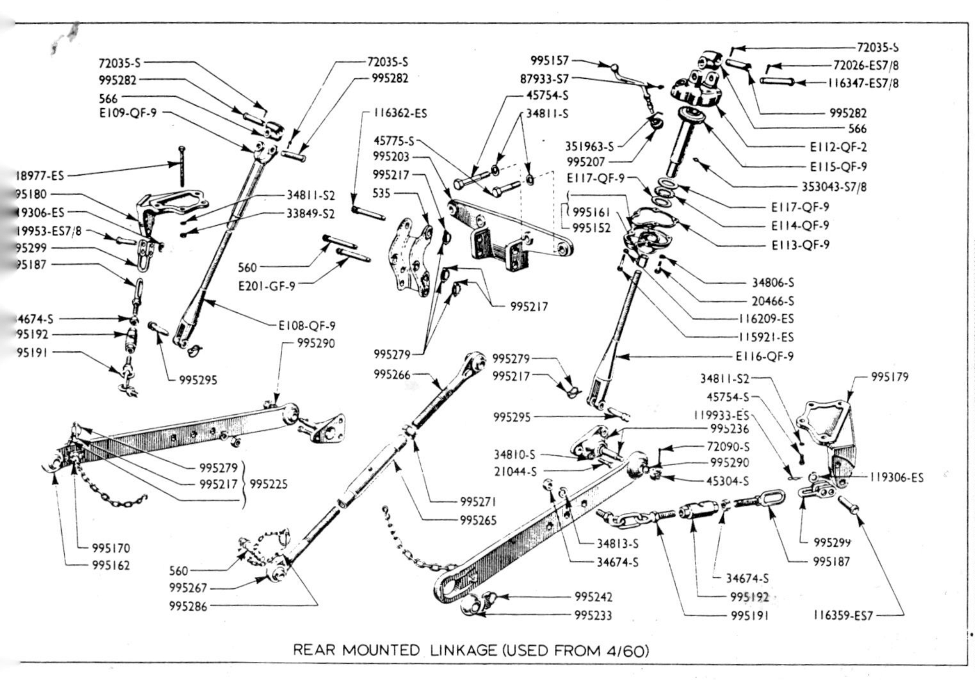

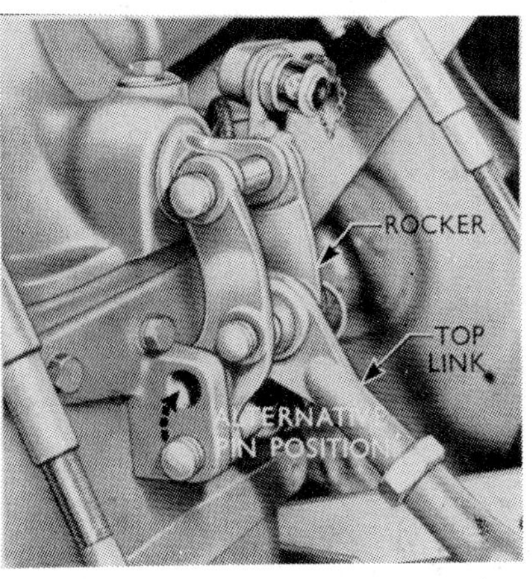

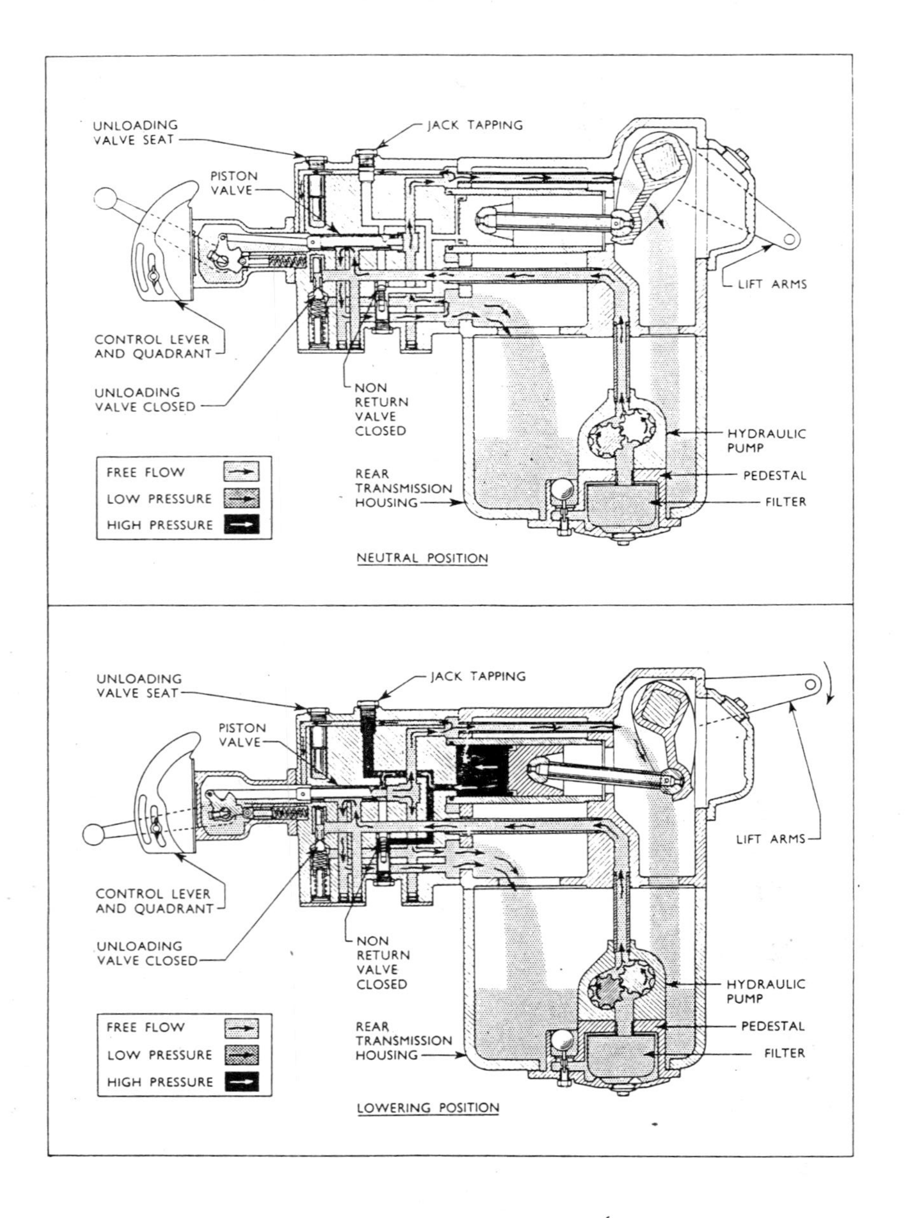

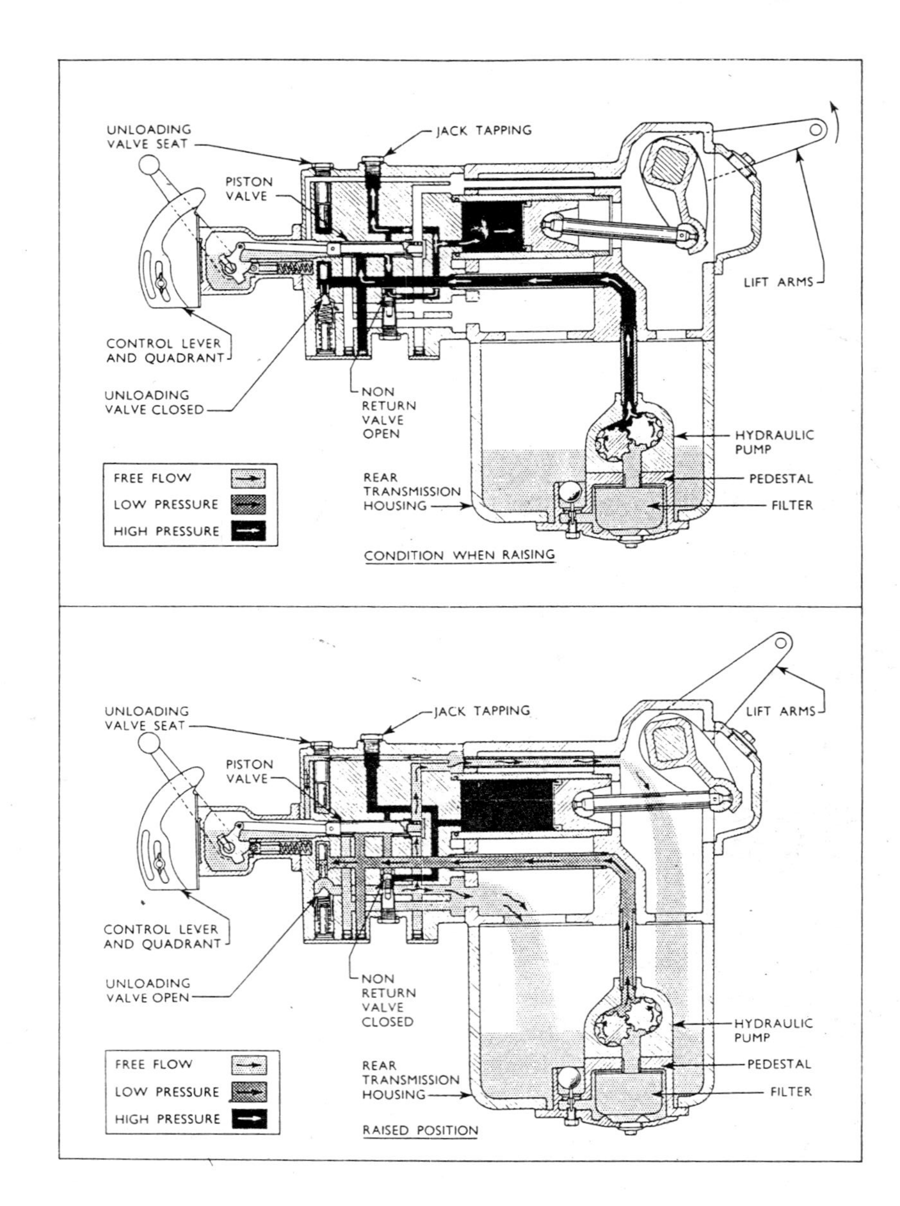

These diagrams are self explanatory and show the flow of oil during operation of the Hydraulic Power Lift.

Above: The Power Assisted Steering installation.

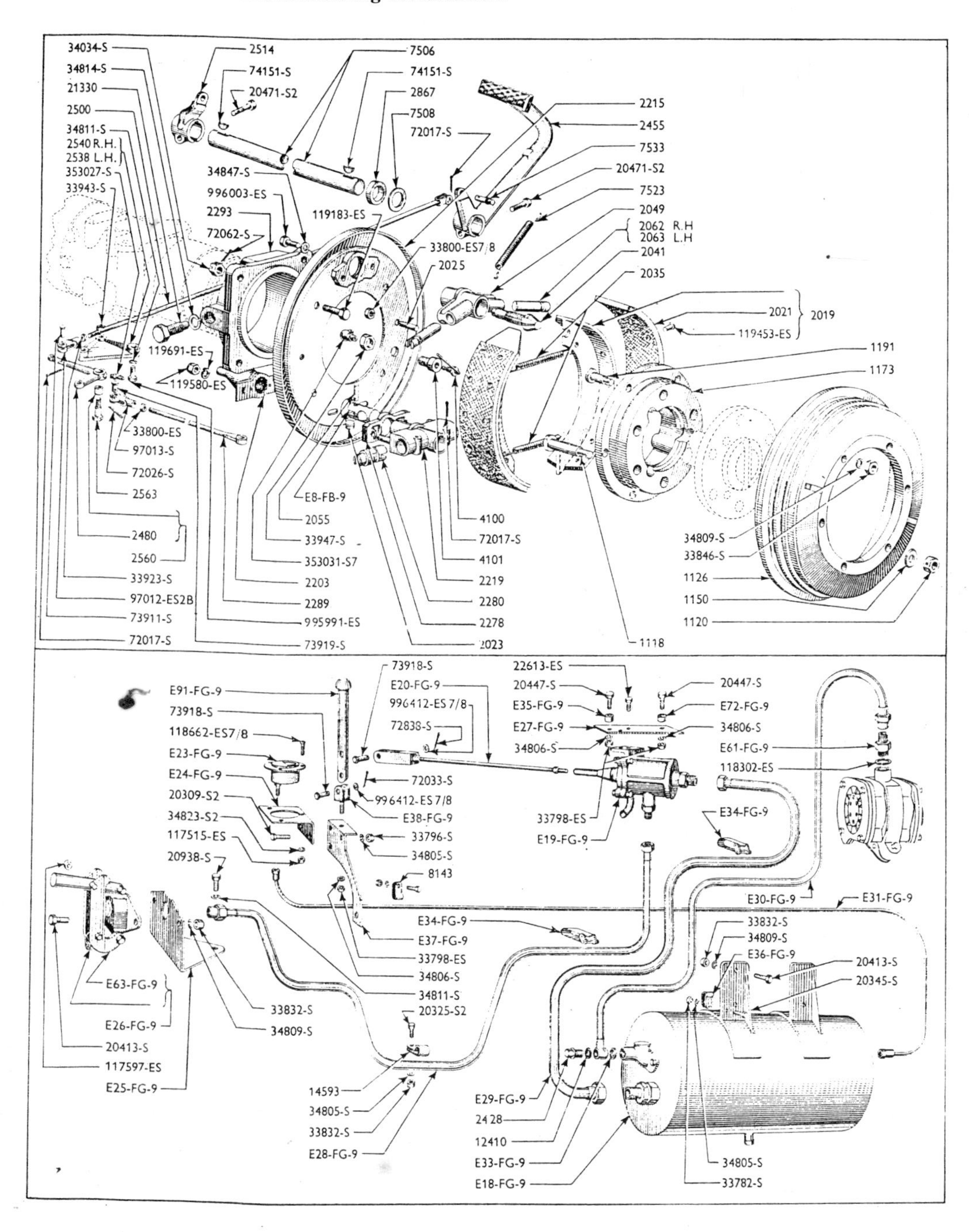

***Right:* The rear wheel brakes fitted to Industrial tractors.**

***Right:* Trailer vacuum equipment was available as an option with engine driven exhauster.**

Instrumentation and Accessories.

The New Major instrument panel only incorporated an ammeter and temperature gauge. An engine hourmeter could be fitted on top of the pump drive line on the RH side of the engine front cover. This same location was later used for the operation of a Proofmeter which was mounted low on the RH side next to the instrument panel; it was introduced as an accessory in 1954 and fitted in production from the following year. With the advent of the Power Major the Proofmeter was located in the new style instrument panel below the steering column on the RH side; The LH circle contained oil pressure and generator warning lights and a temperature gauge much in the style of then current car dash panels.

A toolbox was provided on the LH side of the tractor in front of the starter motor.

The original seat assembly was basically a pressed steel pan which in the case of tractors with hydraulics was bolted to the top of the HPL housing, and when hydraulics were not fitted a deeper seat spring was required. The DeLuxe seat was available as an accessory from the mid fifties and incorporated a Dunlopillo squab and back rest covered in blue rexine with orange piping until the advent of the New Performance Super Major when it became grey with blue piping. Colour did vary according to supply however, and the trimming shop at Dagenham did produce some anachronisms.

Below: Controls and instrumentation of the New Fordson Major to 1958.
A spark ignition tractor is seen here. On diesel tractors the starter control lever was as shown in the next illustration and the engine stop control was fitted in place of the choke.

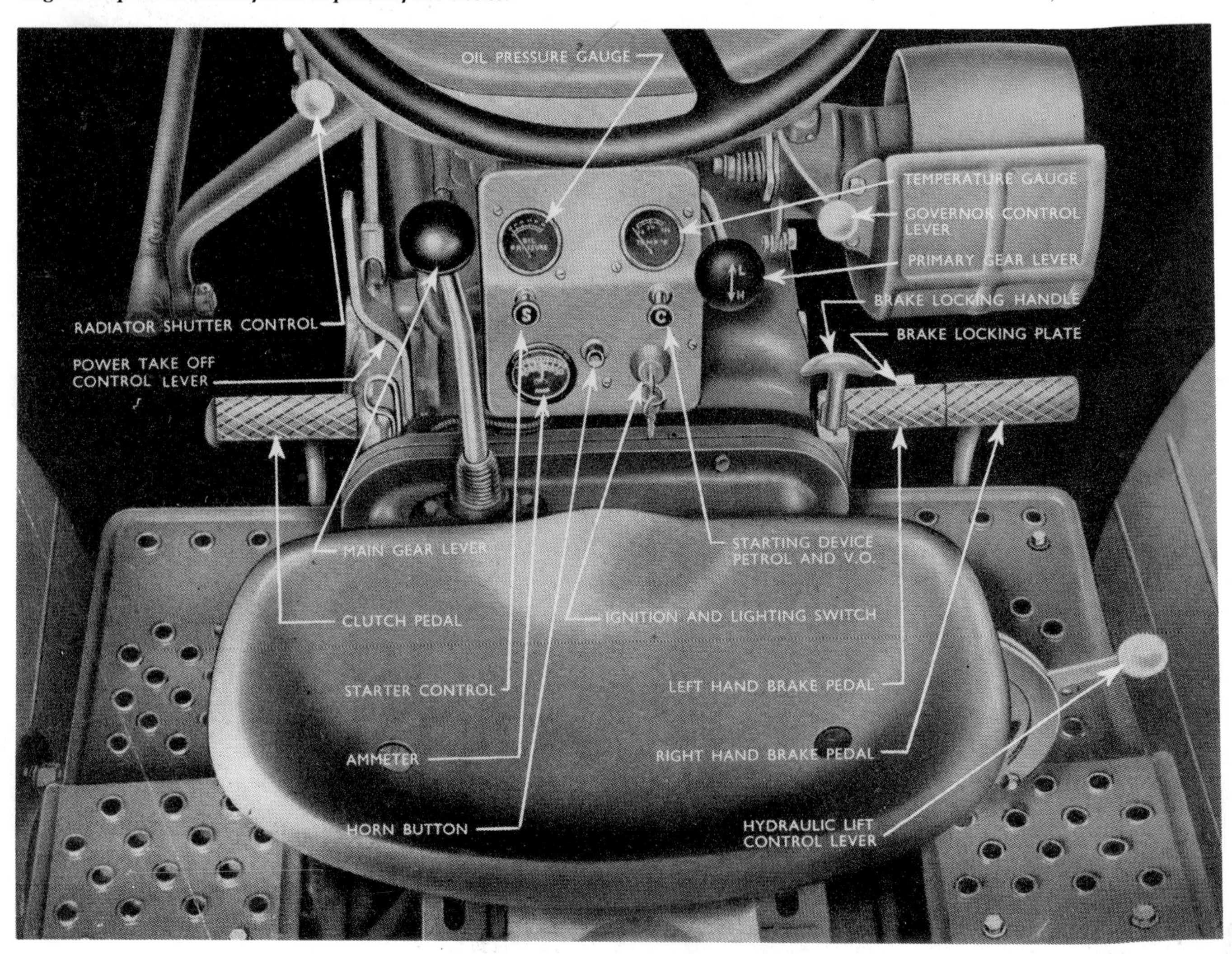

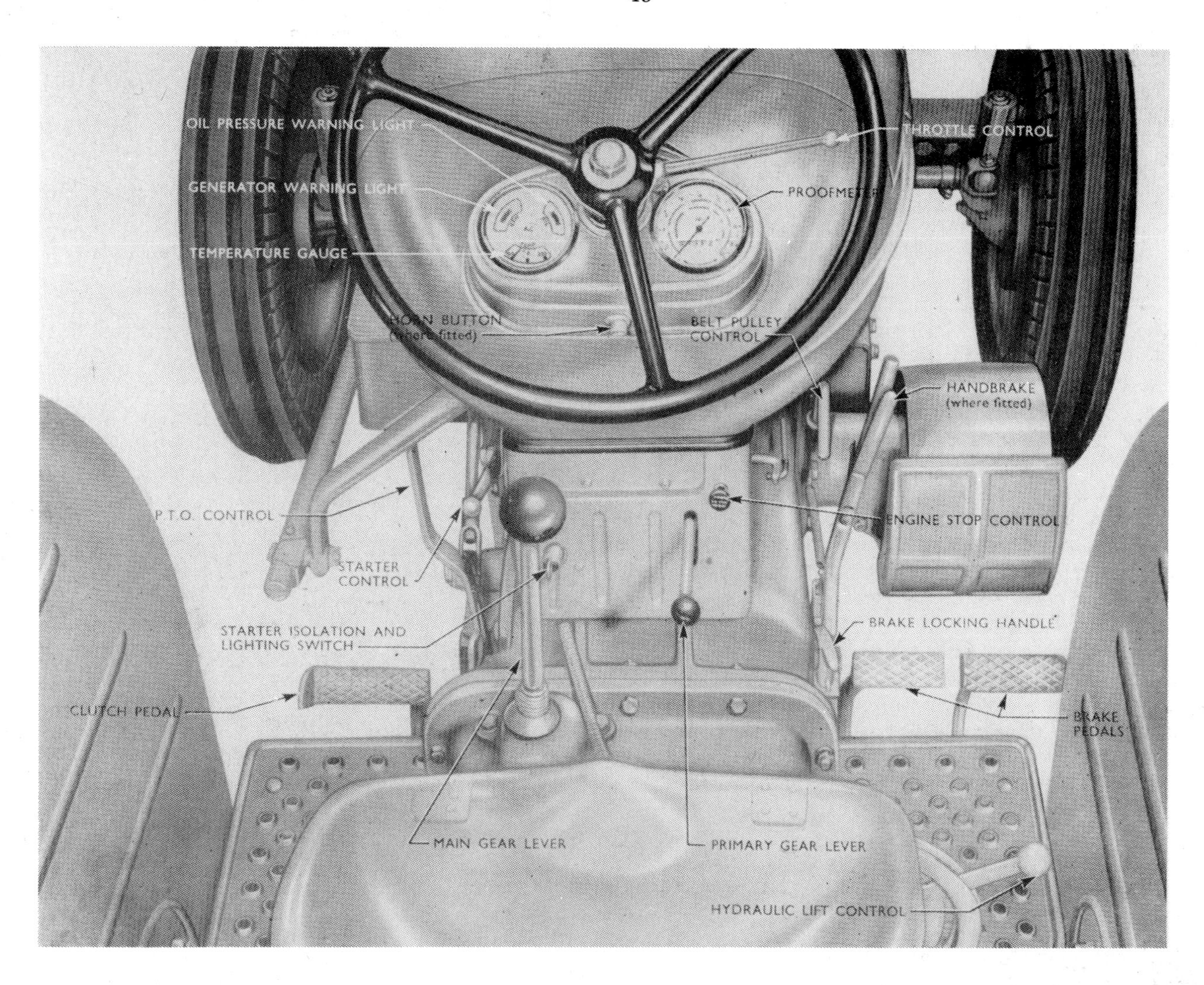

***Above:* Controls and instrumentation on the Power Major 1958-60.**

***Below:* Controls and instrumentation on the Super Major from 1960.**

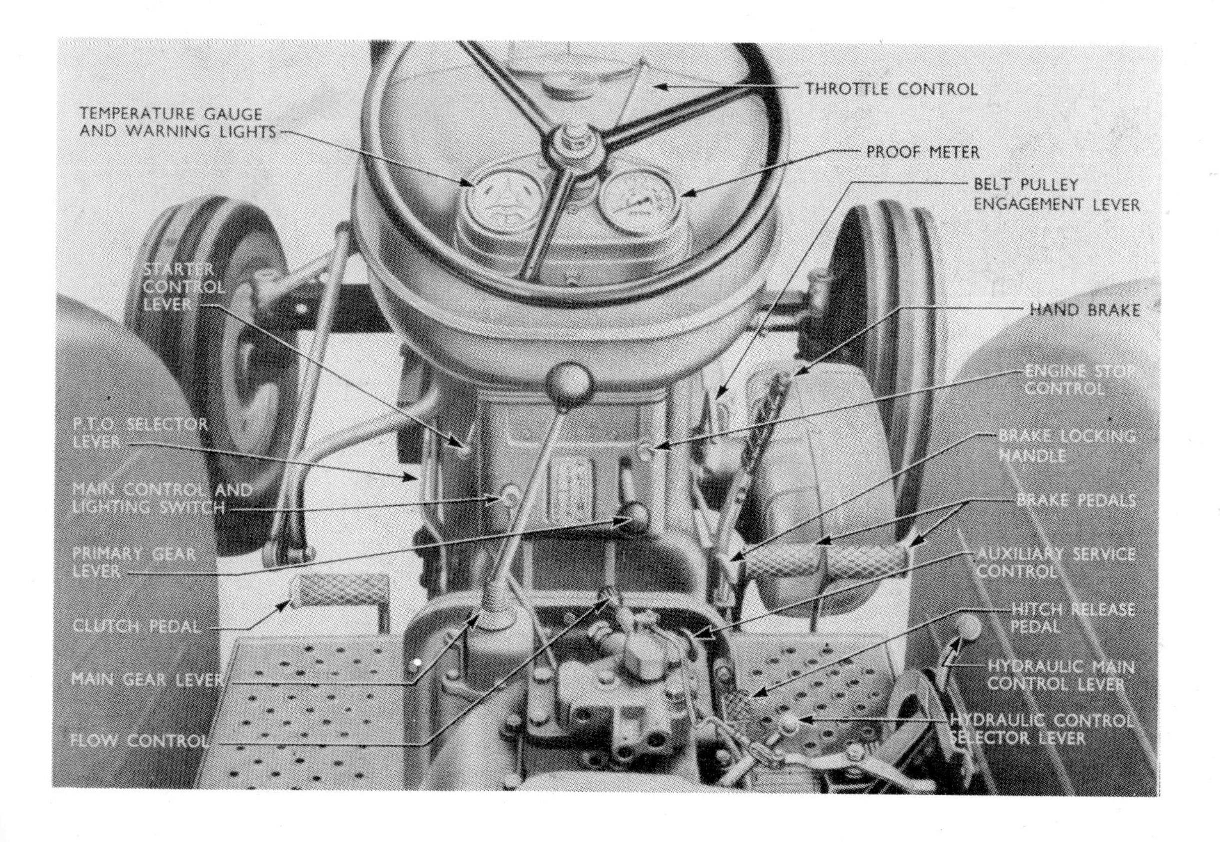

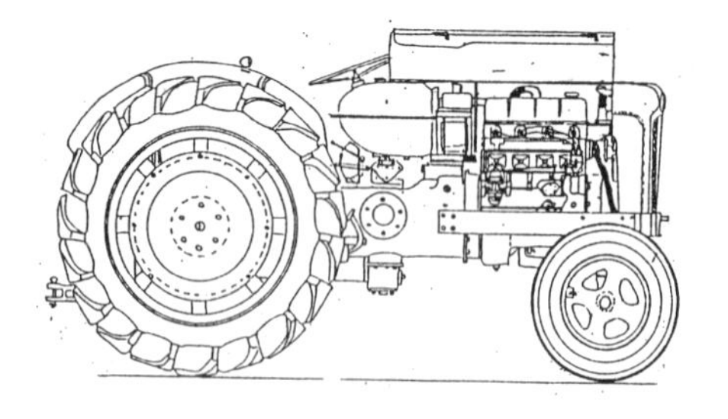

1951 E1ADKN TVO.

The small drawing to the left of each caption shows details which are either special to the tractor illustrated or have changed from the previous drawing. The original spark ignition tractor seen from the offside. Three S.i. tractors were built in December 1951. This is a TVO (E1ADKN) tractor, hence the second filler cap on the tank.

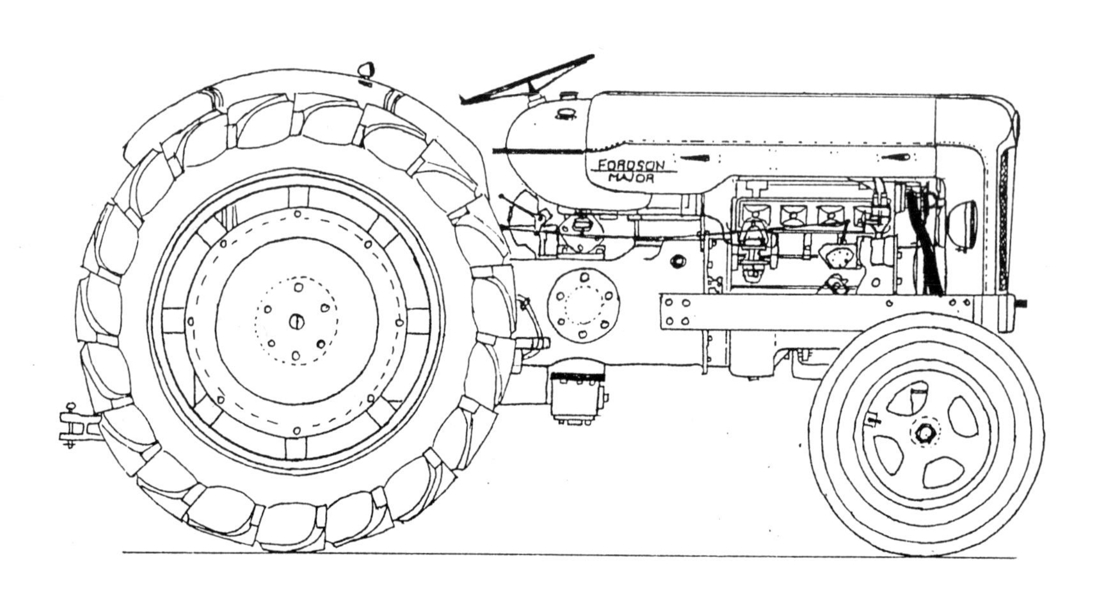

1951-7 E1ADKN TVO & E1ADN PETROL.

The nearside of the S.i. tractor. The radiator shutter control and direct starter motor can be seen. Although S.i. tractors were built right until 1964, the TVO version was discontinued after 1957, leaving only the Petrol (E1ADN) model available; very few of the latter were sold.

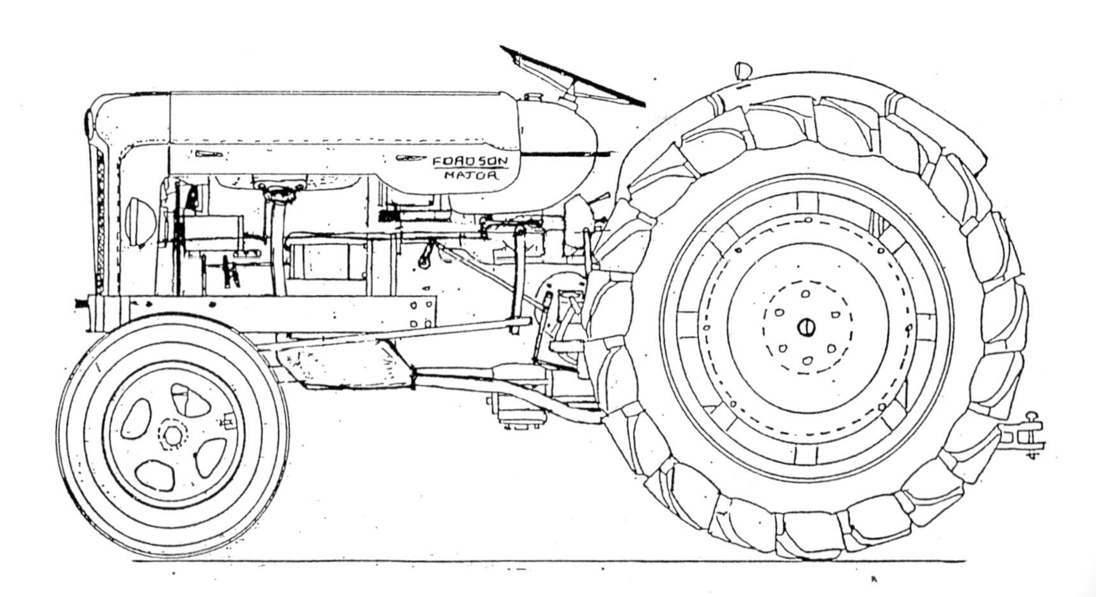

1952 E1ADDN DIESEL.

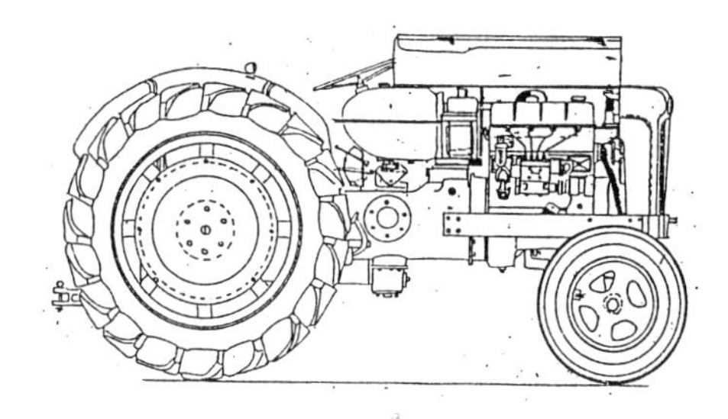

The original diesel tractor. Note the vertical injection pump with four bolts on the cover, lack of vertical exhaust and air intake pipes, and the bonnet badge with 'Diesel' added below.

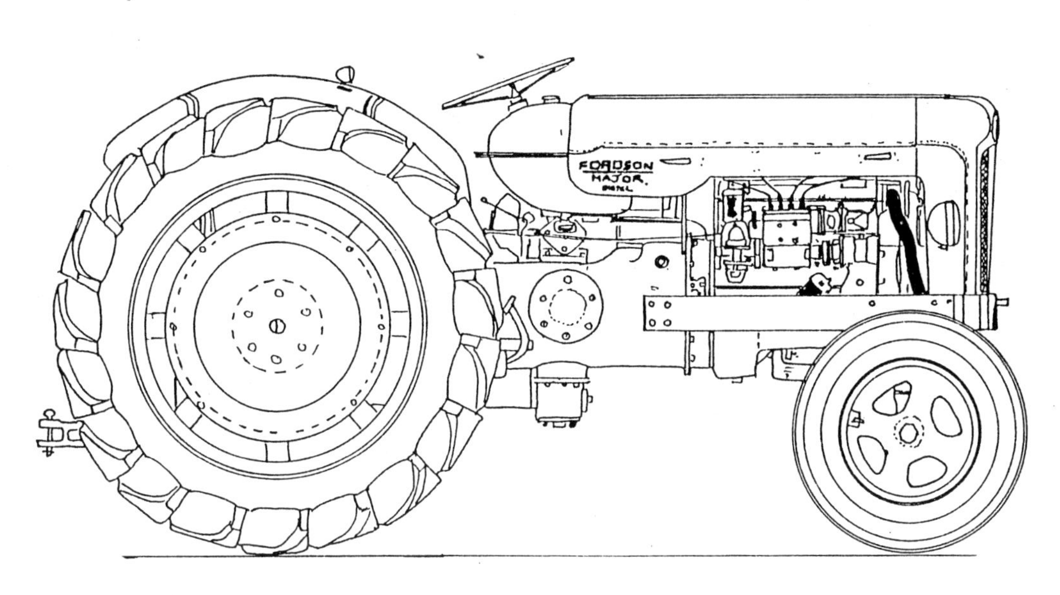

1952 E1ADDN DIESEL.

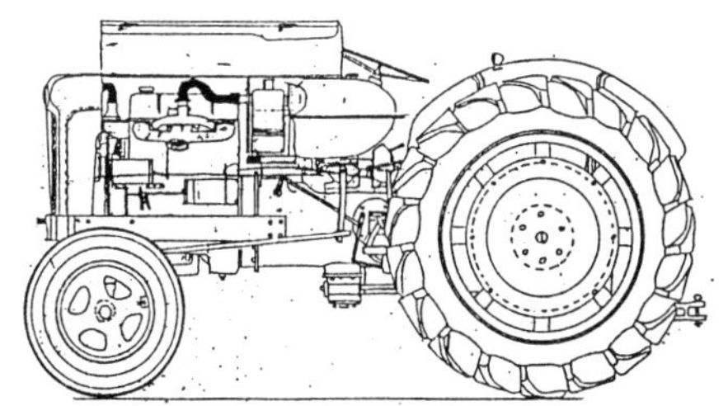

The diesel tractor from the nearside showing the starter control, radiator shutter control, clutch operating linkage, and other details.

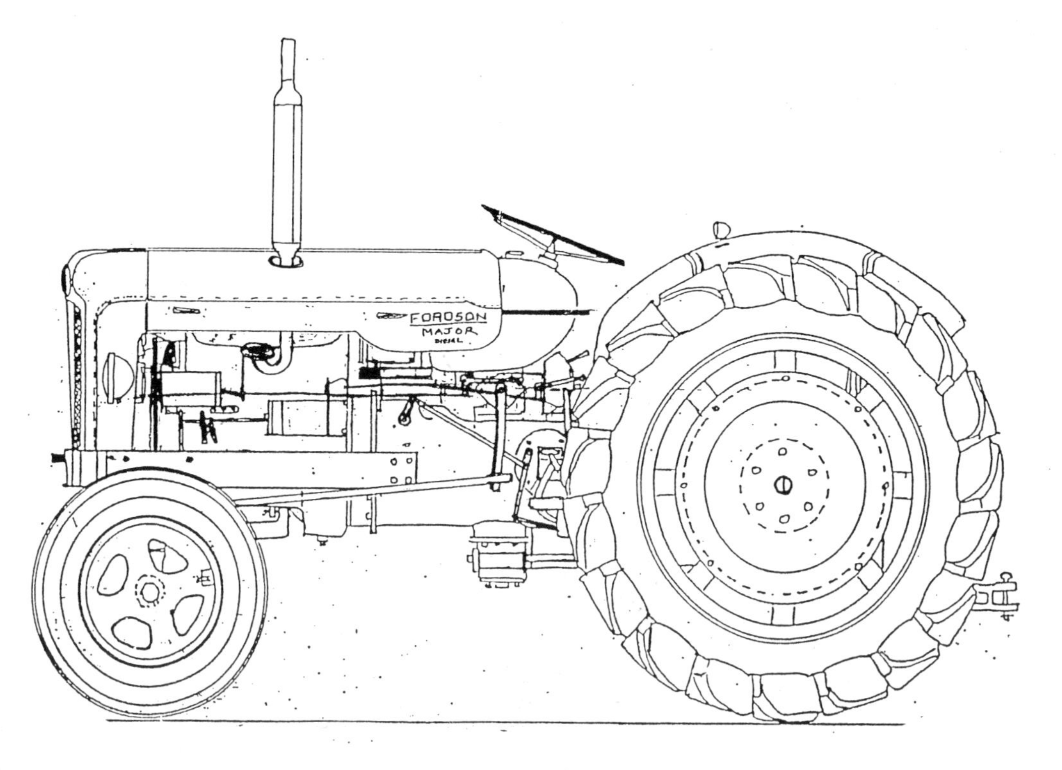

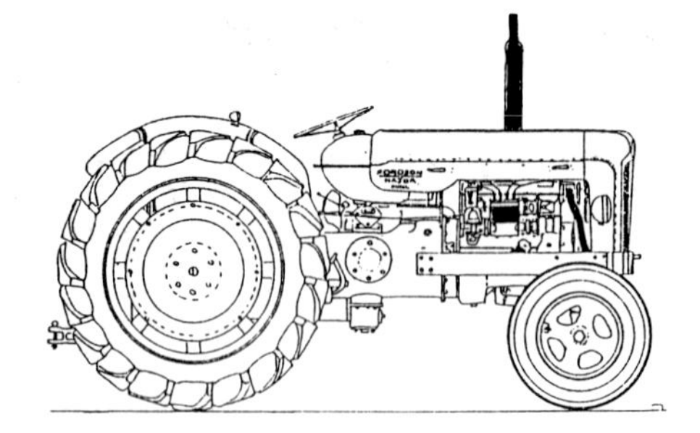

Mid. 1954 E1ADDN.

This December 1953 tractor has the modified cover on the Injection Pump, plus a vertical exhaust.

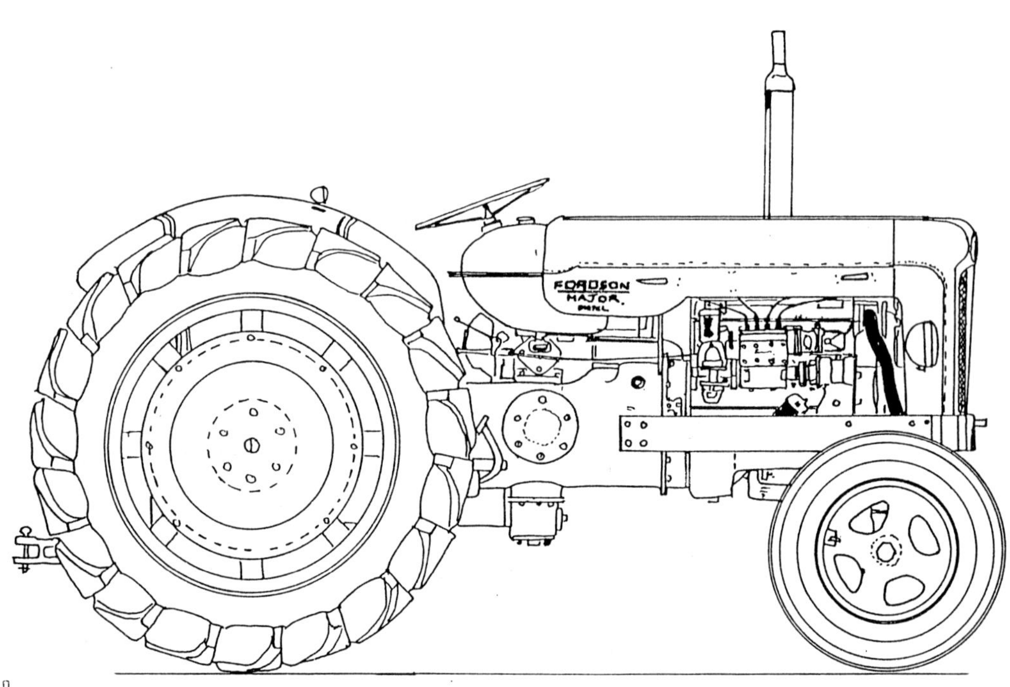

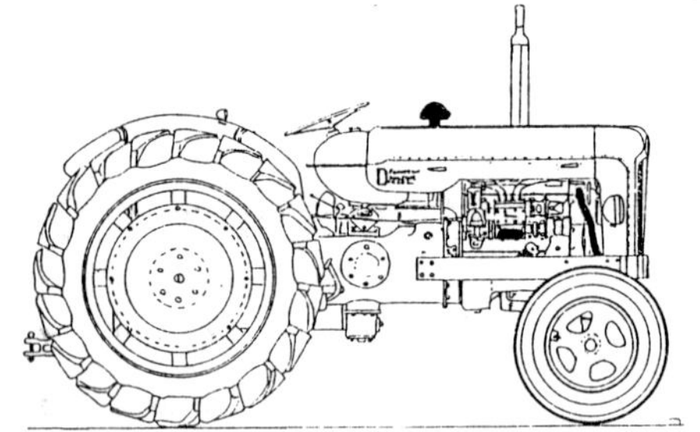

Late 1953 E1ADDN.

This 1954 tractor has the inclined injection pump, and external primary cleaner.

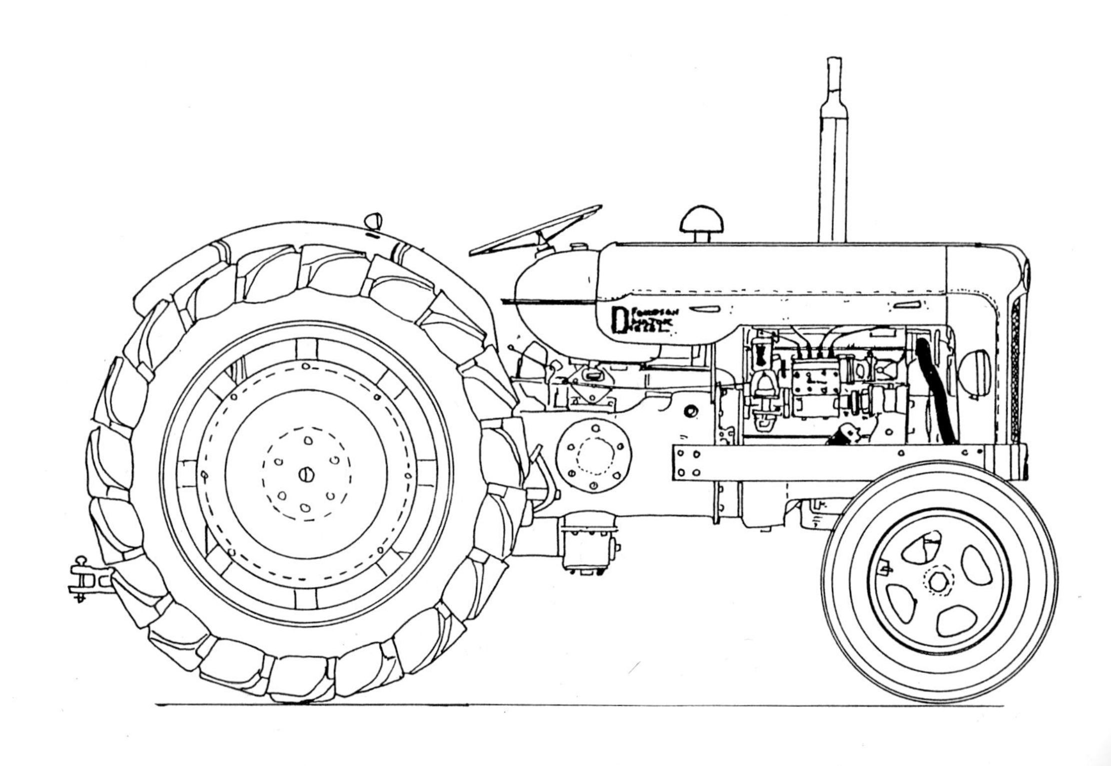

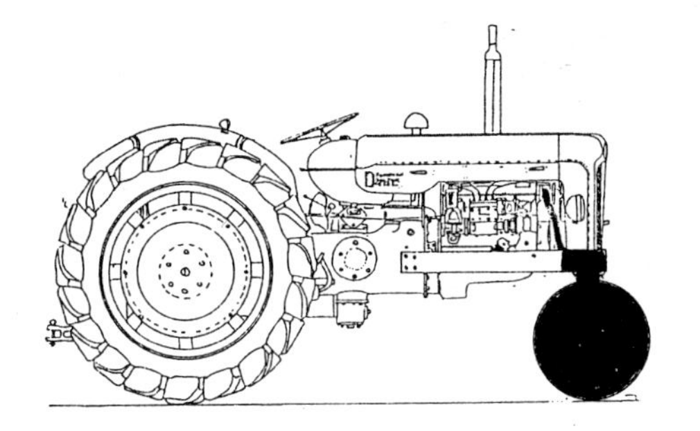

1954 E1ADDN with Rowcrop front end.

For export a vee front twin wheel assembly was manufactured for Ford by Roadless and this diesel engined tractor is so fitted. Standard front wheel size was 6.00 x 16" and the rear size the usual 11 x 36" although 11 x 38" rims were available as an option.

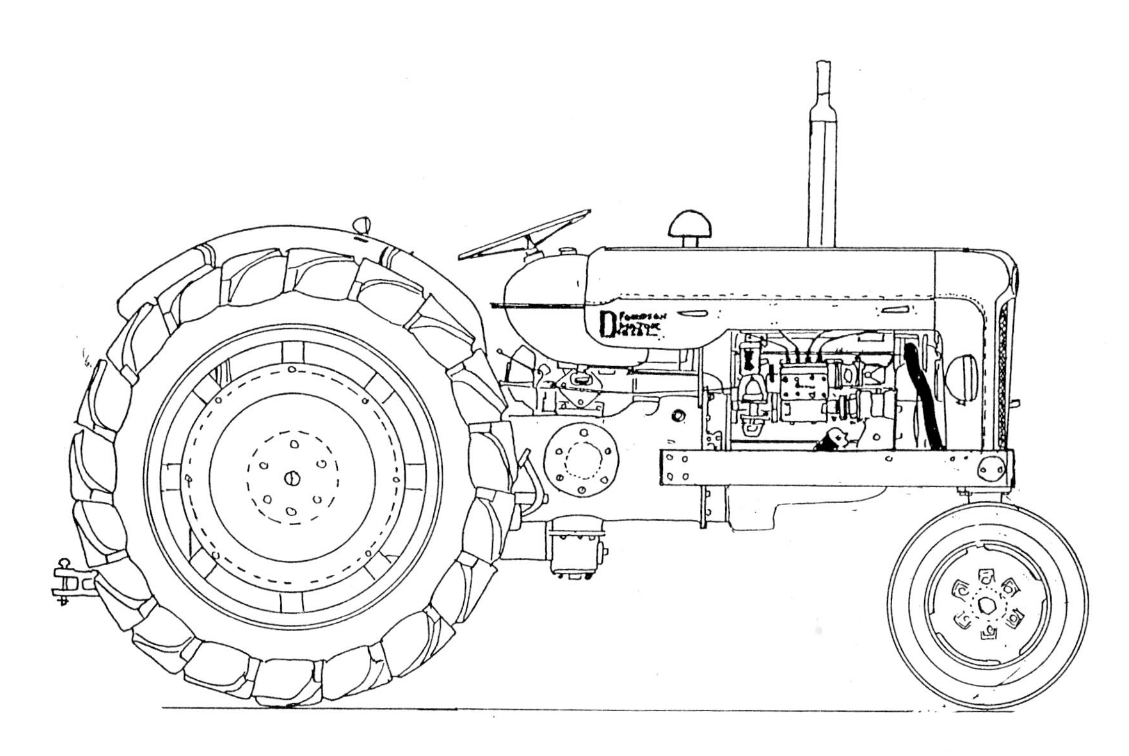

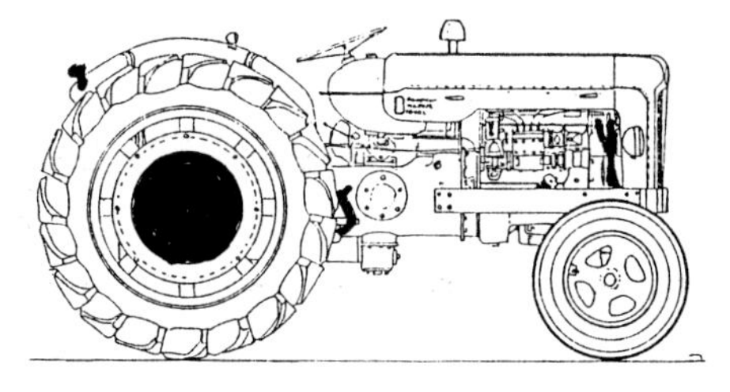

Late 1954 E1ADDN Industrial.

By 1954 lighting regulations required the fitting of two rear lamps and late in the year a narrow fan belt with necessary modifications to pulleys etc. was introduced. An industrial model is illustrated here with rear wheel brakes and rear towing attachment.

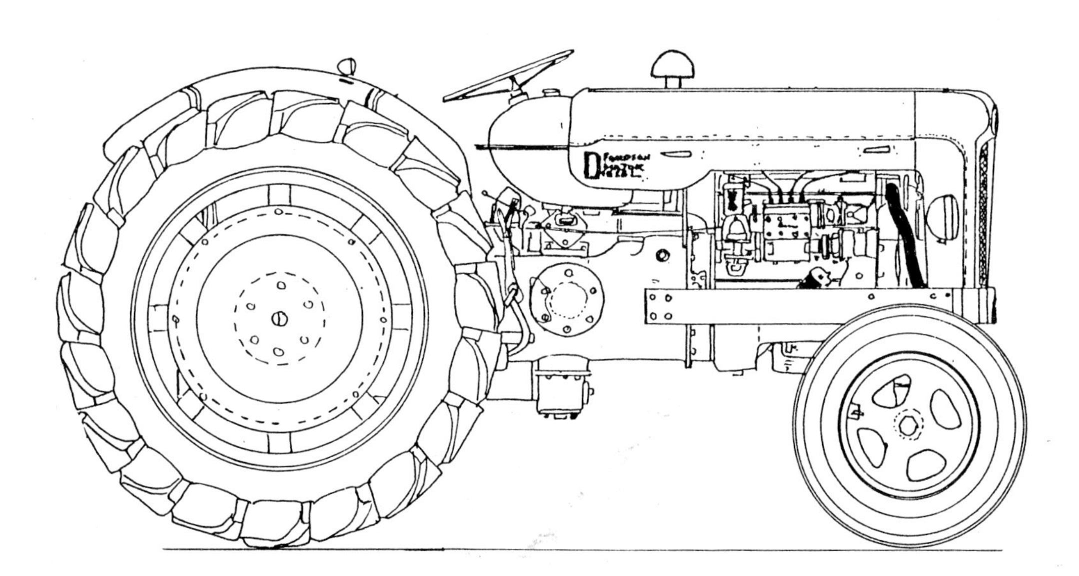

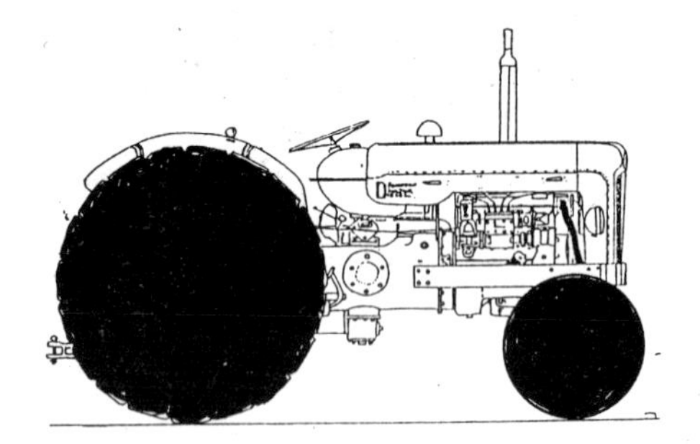

1955 E1ADDN for Export.

For export, oversize tyres were offered, although some contractors managed to get them on 'home' models. Here 7.50 x 16" front and 14 x 30" rear tyres are fitted.

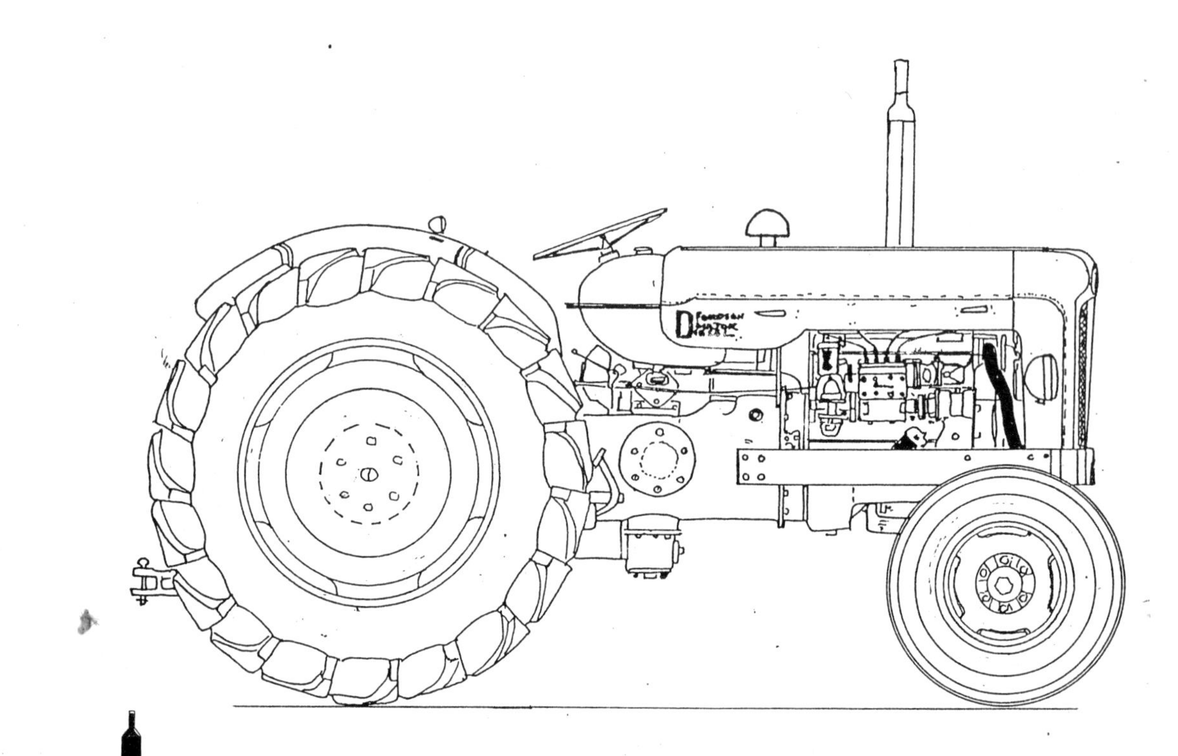

1955 E1ADDN Australia.

Australian tractors however were shipped in a knocked down state less wheels and still featured home fitted cast centres. Note also the Huba Spark arrester fitted to the Antipodean exports on arrival.

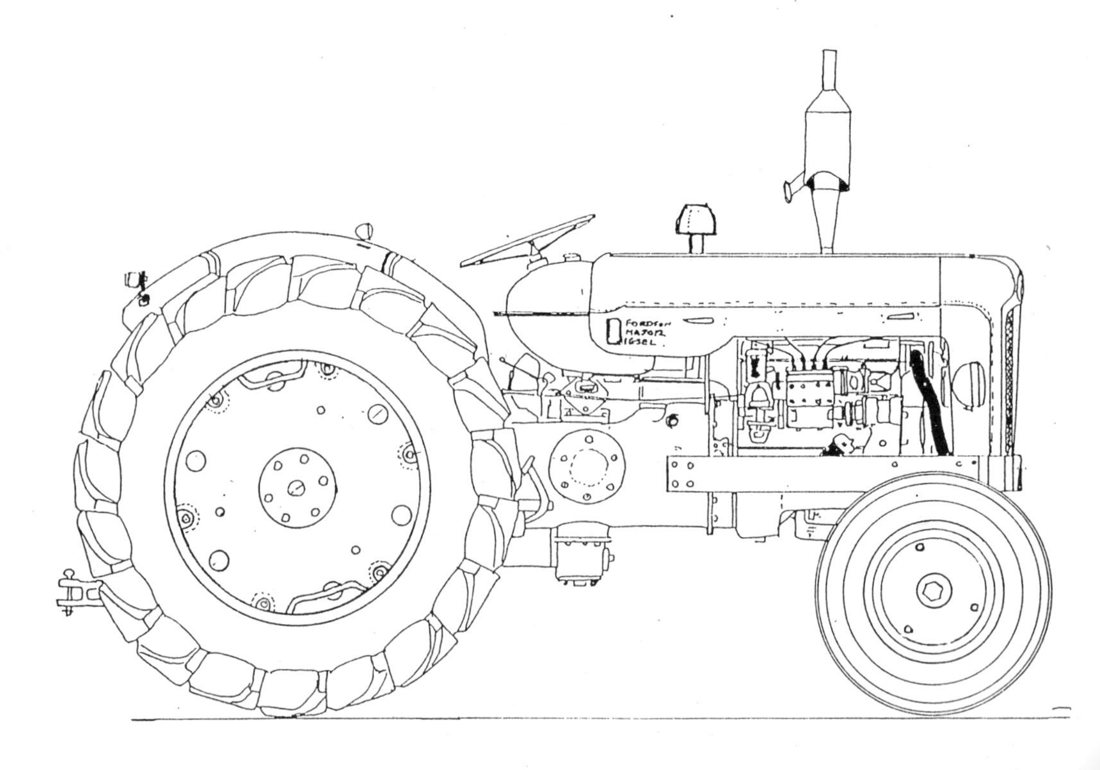

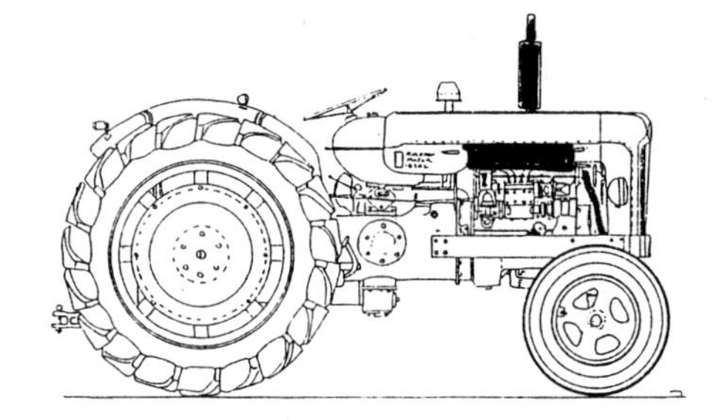

1957 E1ADDN with Mark II engine.

With the introduction of the Mark II engine in 1957 a revised silencer was adopted.

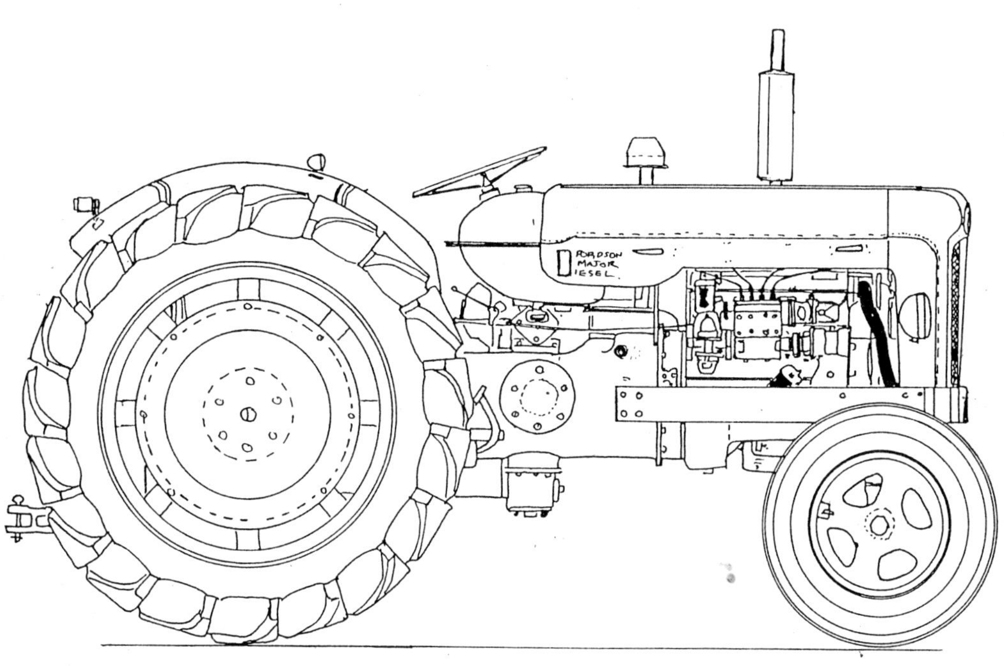

1957 E1ADDN.

The nearside of a 1957 tractor fitted with Mark II engine showing the throttle linkage layout. Radiator shutters had been deleted from earlier in 1957.

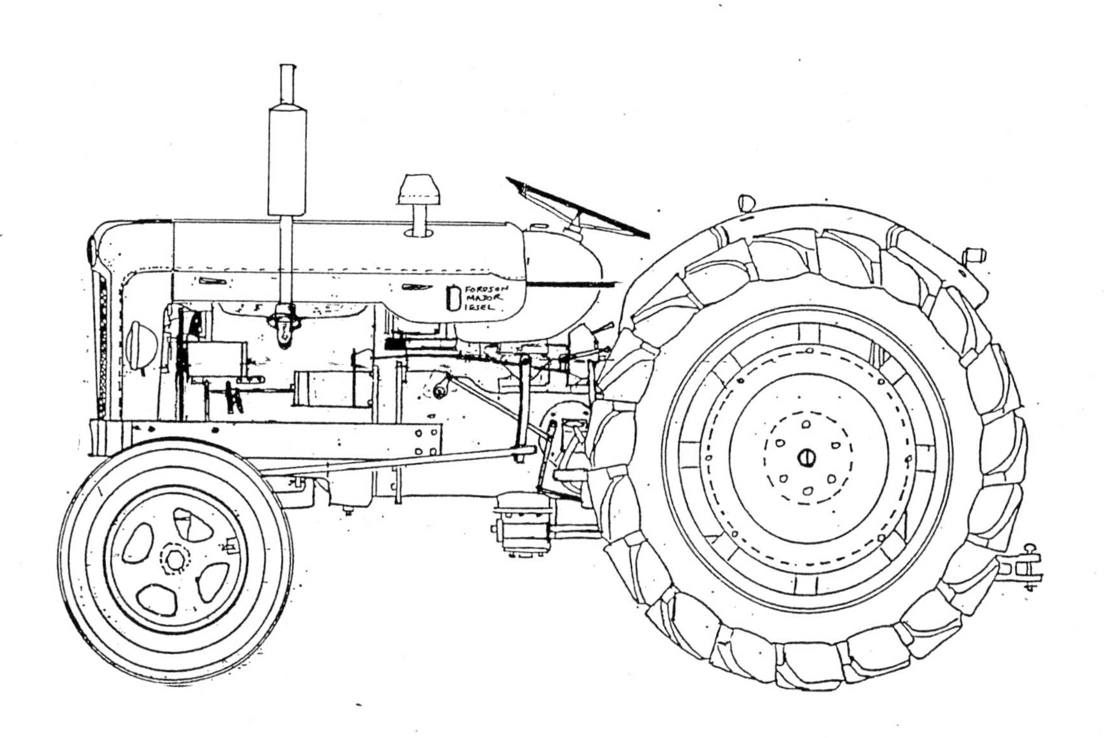

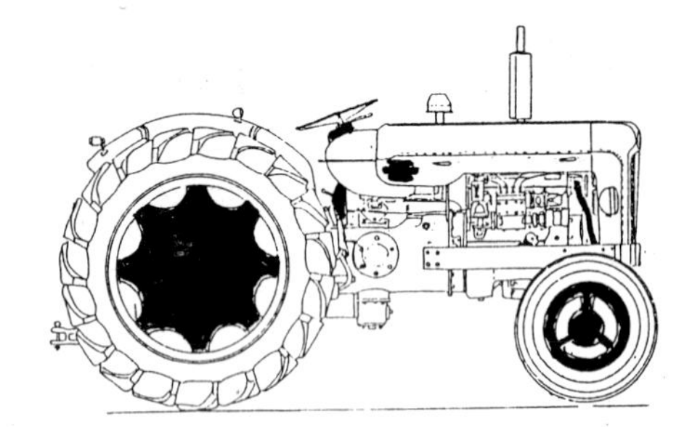

1958 Power Major.

The Power Major was introduced in August 1958 and the detail revisions are highlighted in the key drawing to the left. Note the revised wheel design, the improved control layout, and new badging.

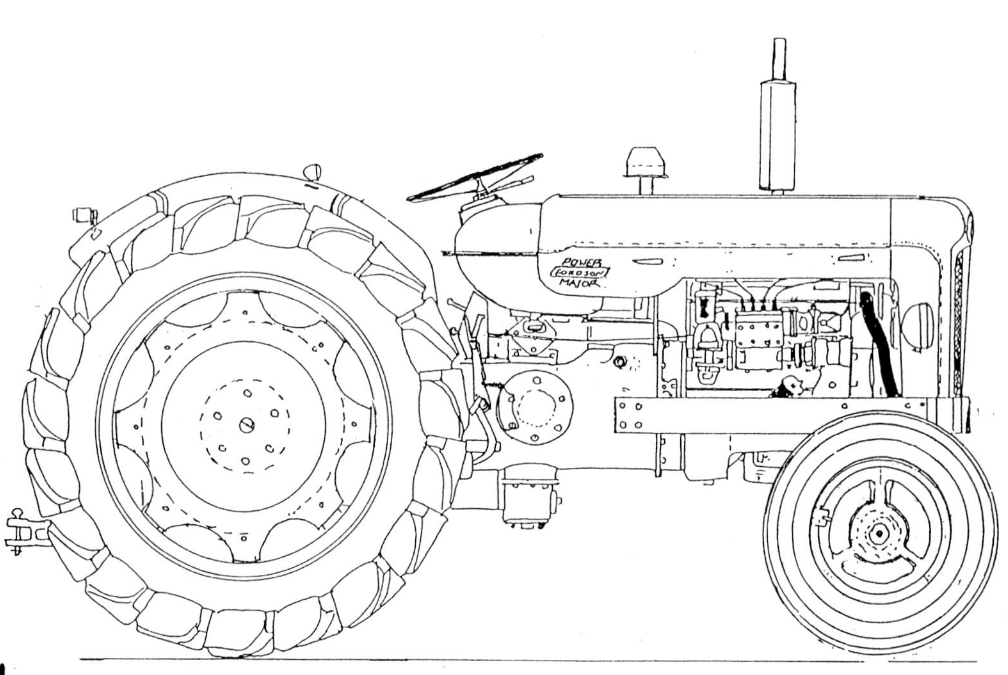

1960 Super Major.

The Super Major was launched at Smithfield Show in December 1960. Improved hydraulics and brakes, plus differential lock were the main 'selling' points. The headlamps were recessed into the front grilles.
Early tractors retained the pneumatically governed Simms injection pump.

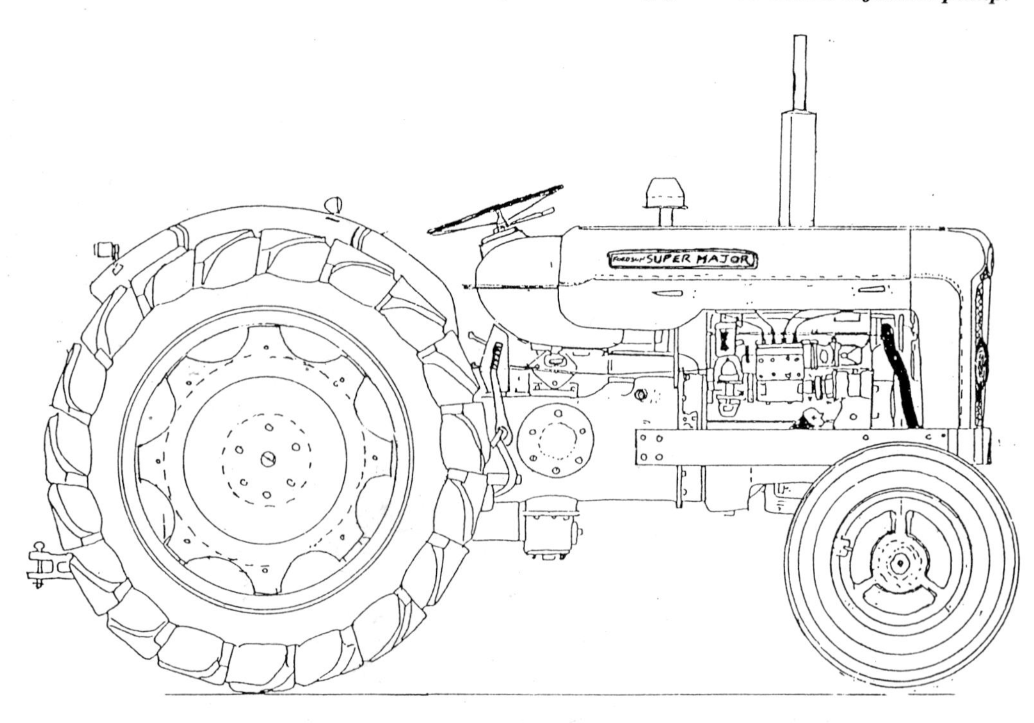

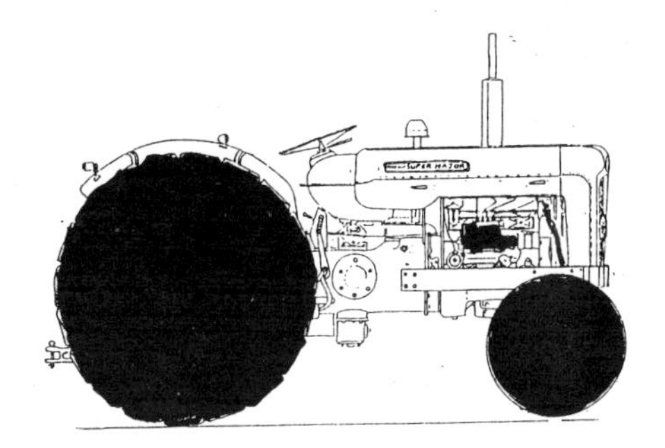

1962 Super Major with tyre options.

Optional wheel and tyre equipment was available on all Super Majors, and can be seen here, the front wheels being 7.50 x 16" and the rear wheels 14 x 30". From May 1962 the Simms 'Minimec' fuel injection pump as seen here was fitted; this had a mechanical governor.

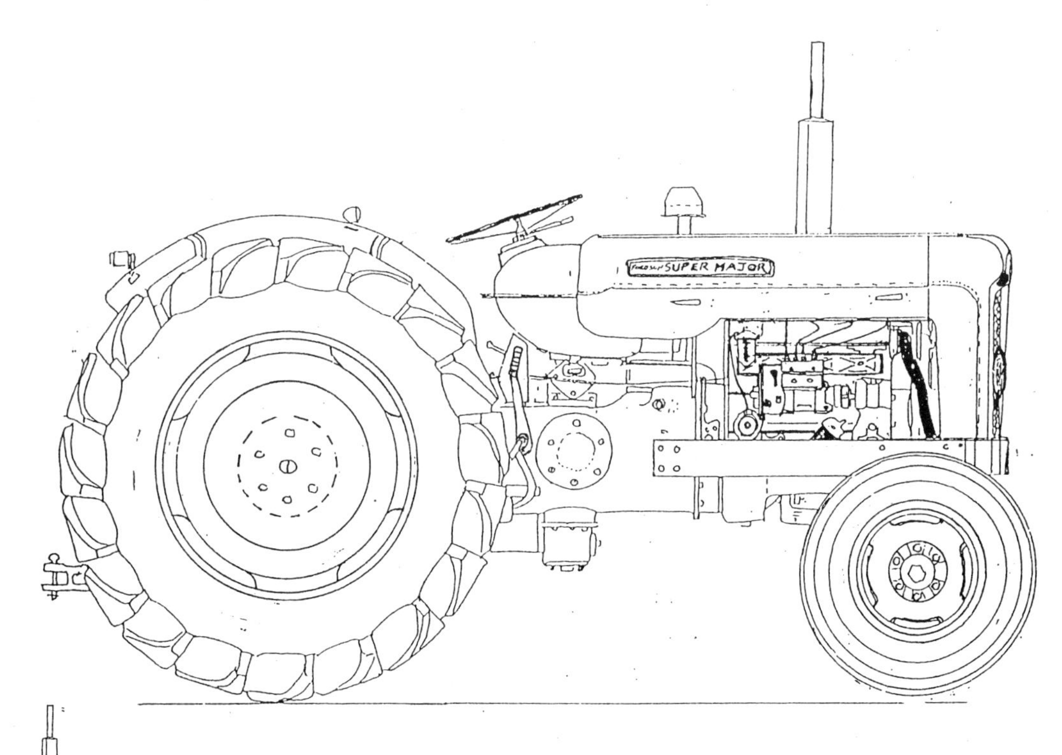

1962 Super Major (export).

Certain export tractors retained outside headlamps and the grilles were reinforced by the addition of three horizontal pressings. Note the absence of handbrake on this example. From 1955 handbrakes were usual on all UK sold tractors although technically a build option.

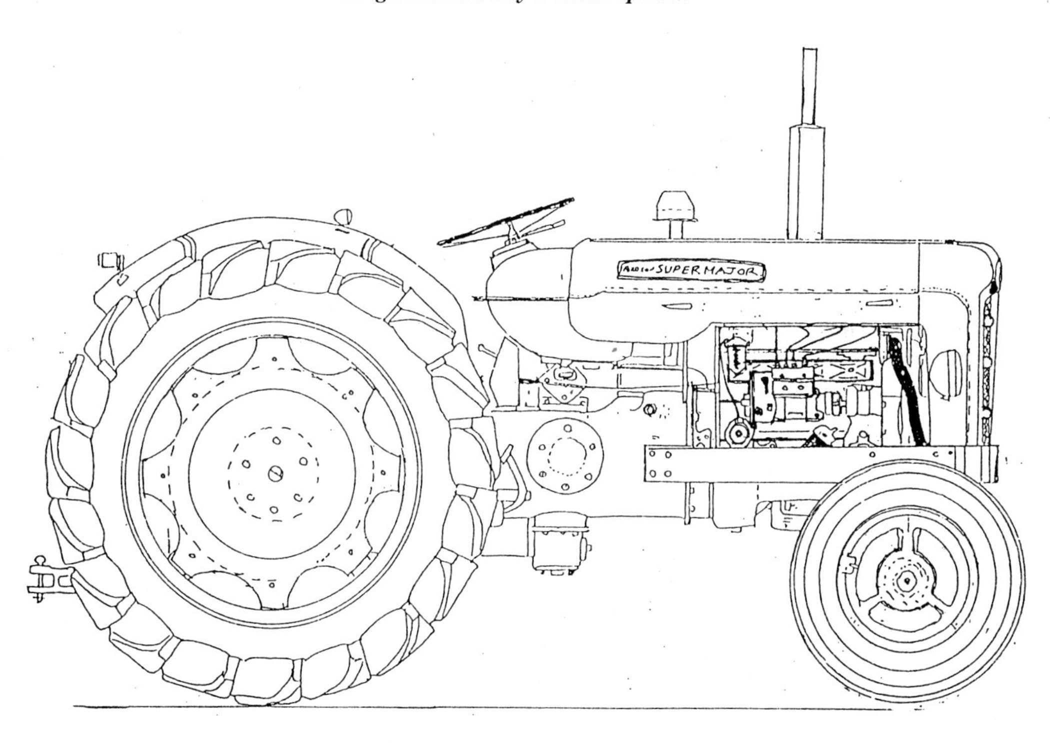

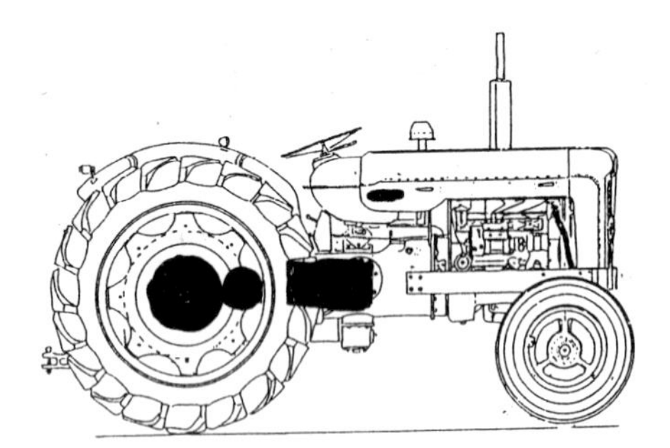

1963 New Performance Super Major.

The New Performance Super Major launched in July 1963 offered slightly more engine power and a new paint job with grey wheel centres and fenders.

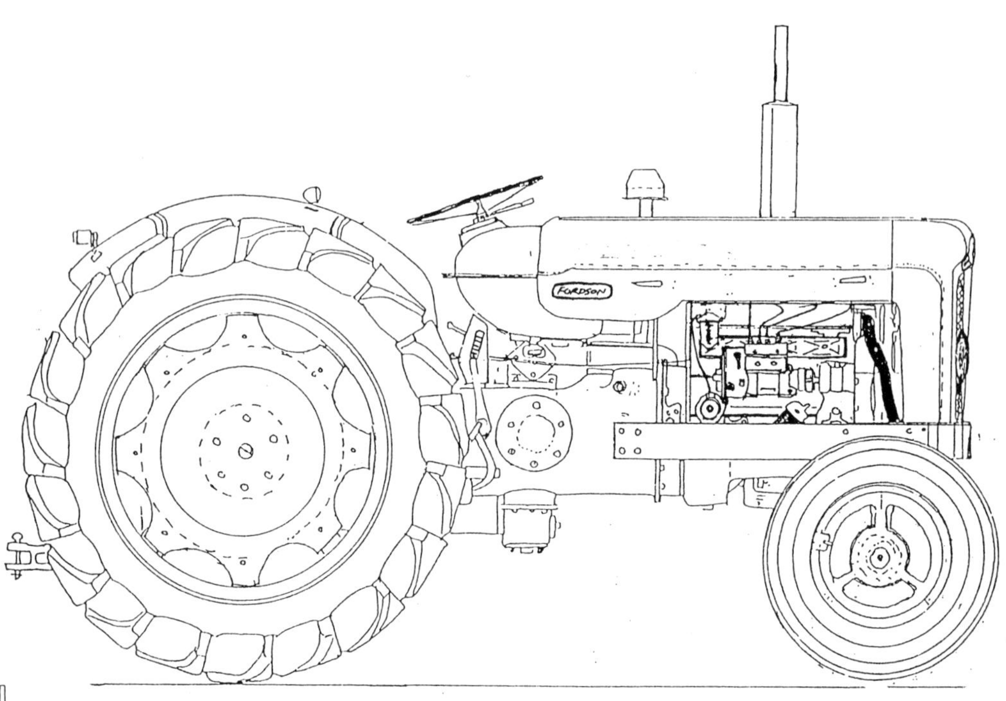

1963 Ford Diesel 5000 for USA.

For 'Across the pond' consumption tractors sold in the USA were given a unique paint job from 1962, with cream/beize bonnet. The decals read 'Ford Diesel 5000 to fit the popular model into the American 2000/4000 range of 1962/4. For details of American built Ford tractors built at the same time as the tractors featured in this book, 'Vintage Tractor Special - 9; American Fordson & Ford is available.

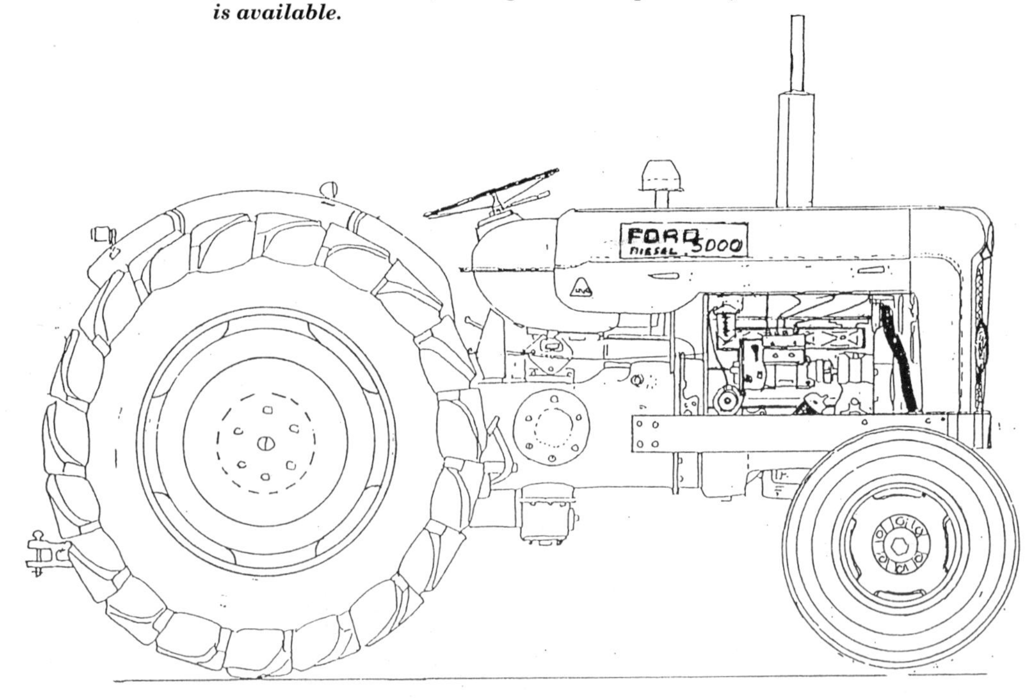

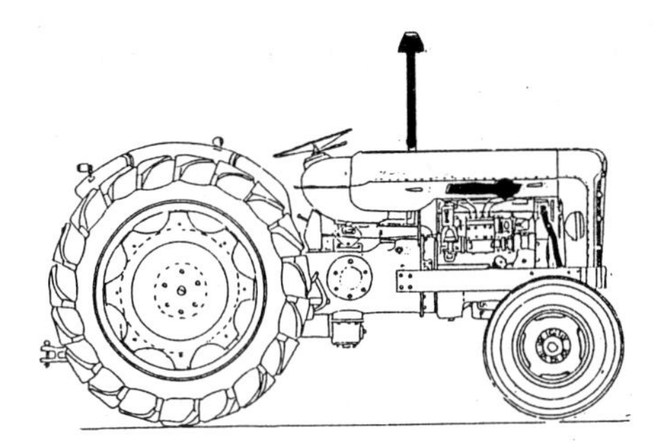

1966 Ebro 160E (built in Spain).

Initial Spanish assembly produced the Ebro Super 55; note the old style injection pump!

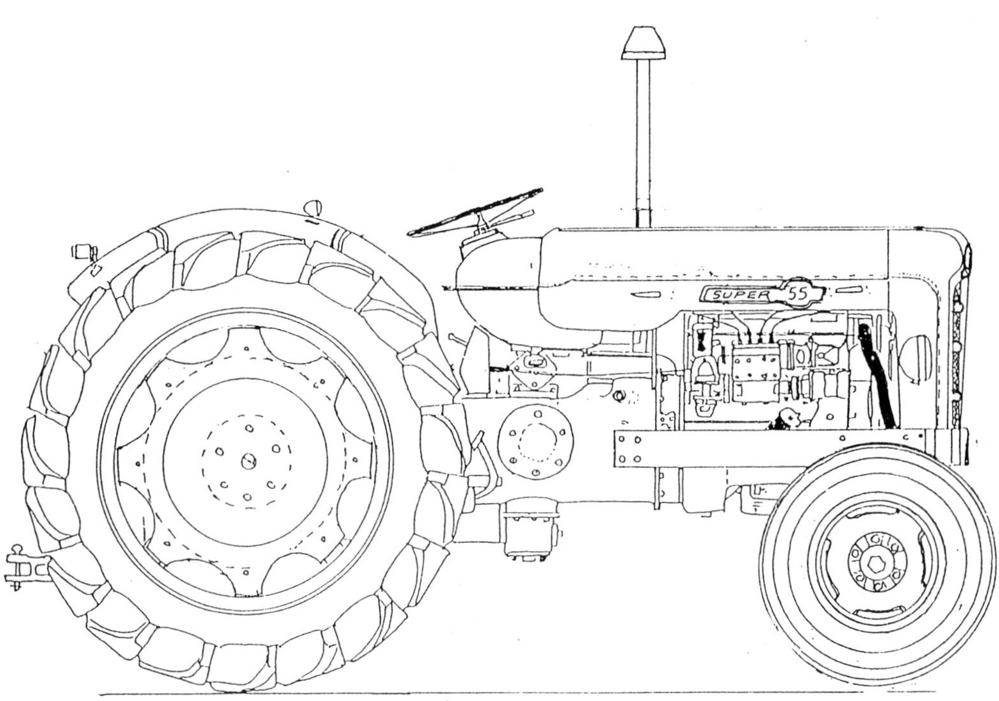

1969 Ebro 155.

The involvement of Massey Ferguson in Ebro from 1966 resulted in this 'hybrid' which was none other than our faithful 'Super Major' hidden beneath MF '100' series tinwork, and finished in a red and grey colour scheme.

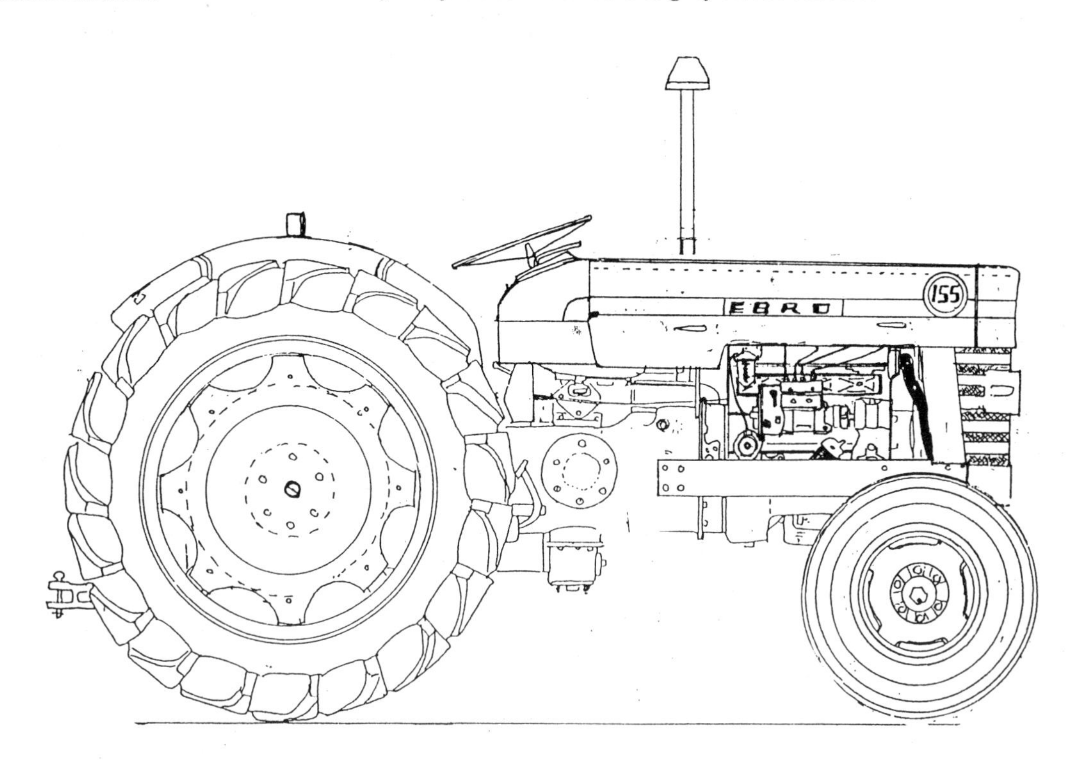

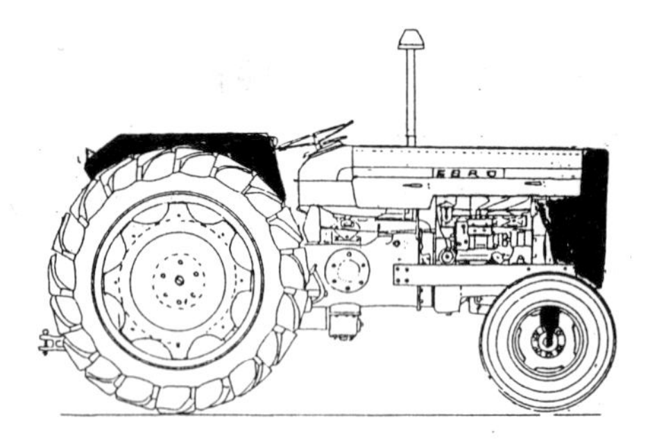

1975 Ebro 160E.

For export the MF '100 series' tinwork was disguised and the tractor offered as the Ebro 160E. Front axle and fenders were however of new design by this time.

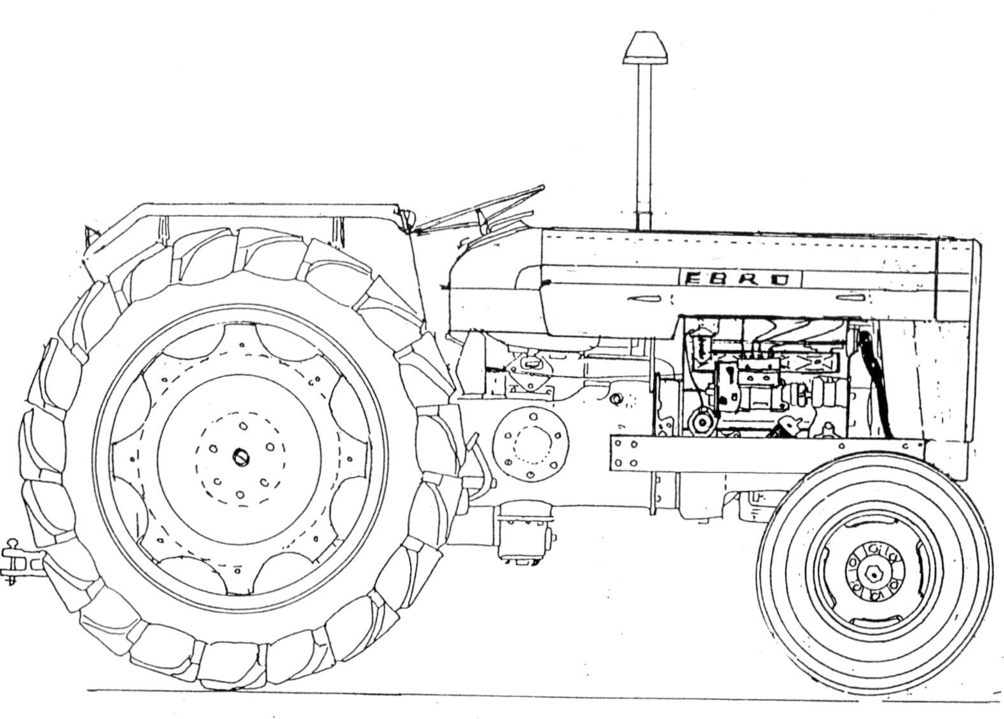

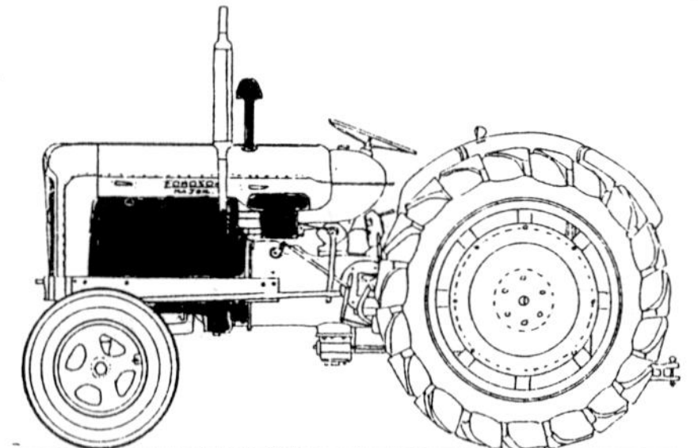

1952 E1ADKN with Perkins L4(TA) conversion 1955.

Shortage of space precludes the illustration of but a few conversions; these will be fully covered in future publications.
Here we have the Perkins L4(TA) engine installed in an E1ADKN tractor.

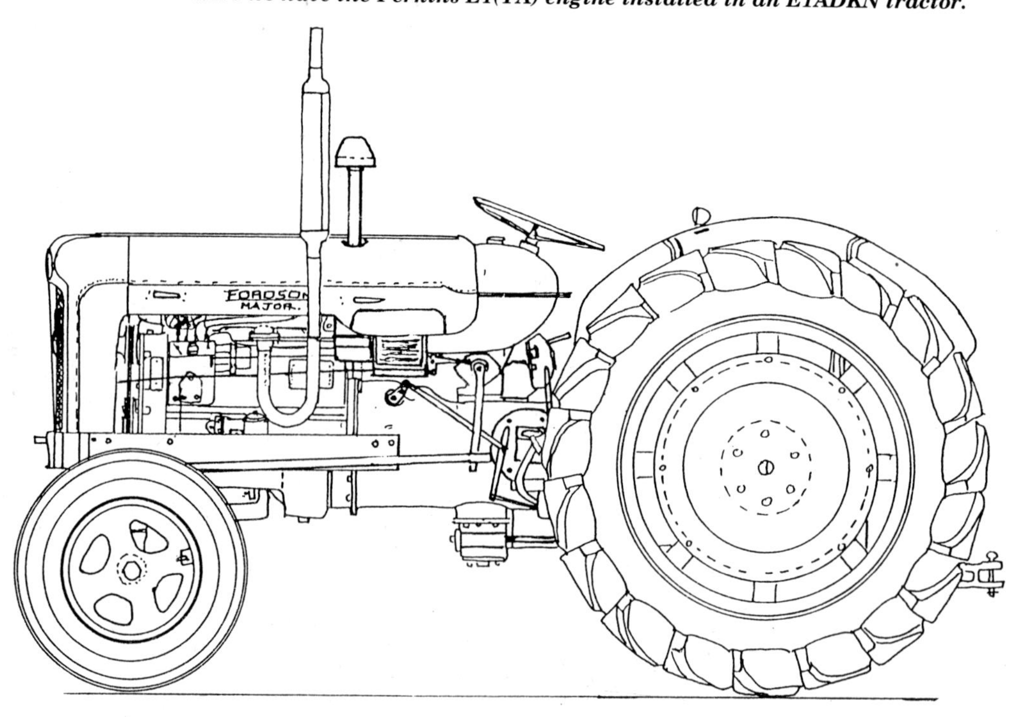

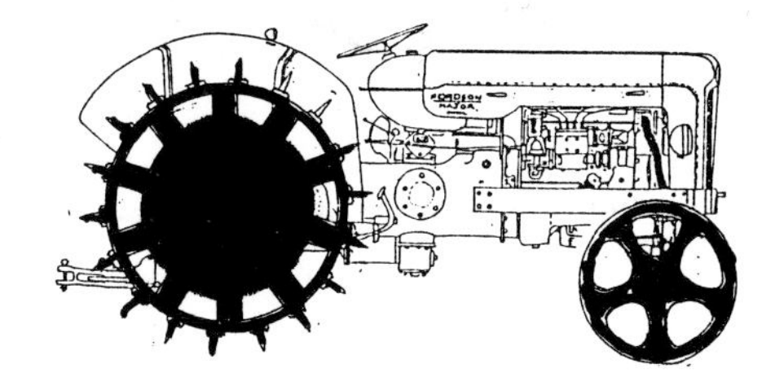

1952 E1ADDN with steel wheels.

Steel wheels were still available on the E1A model and most tractors so fitted were exported.

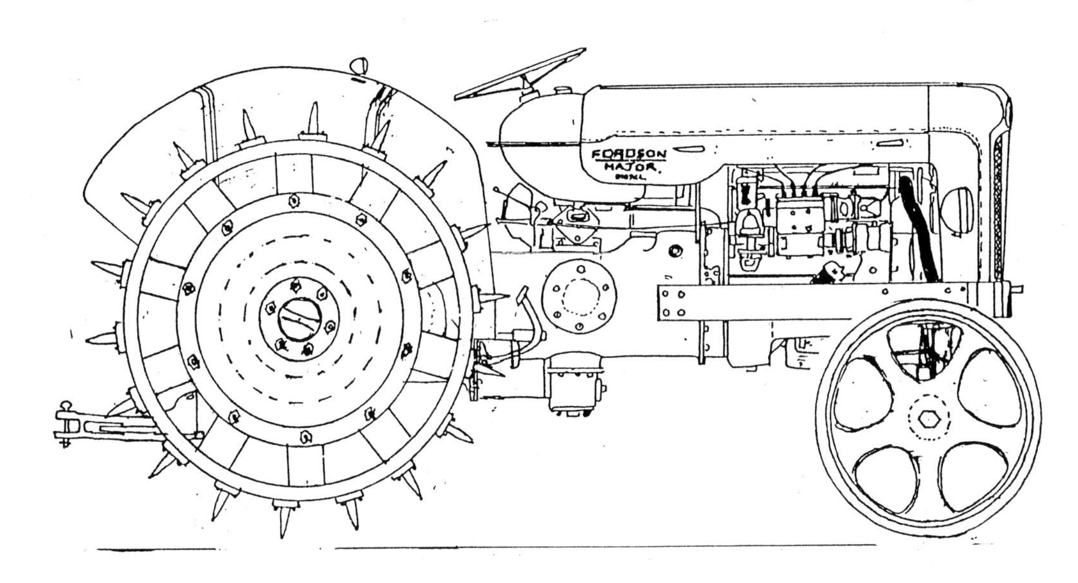

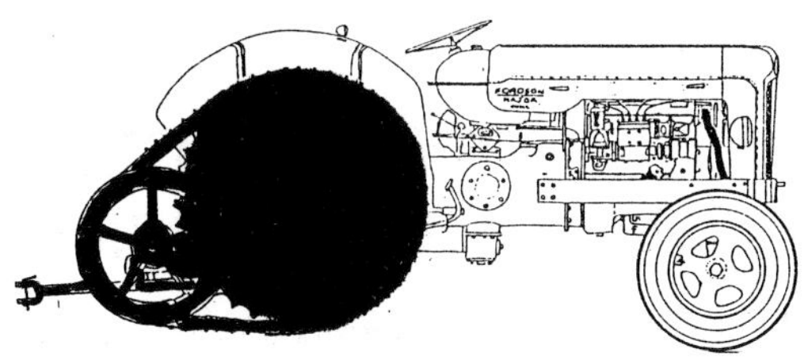

1952 E1ADDN with Roadless DG4 half tracks.

Roadless provided their DG4 tracks for the E1A model. These waned in popularity once Roadless entered the 4WD market. A forthcoming 'Special' on Roadless and County will cover these models in far more detail.

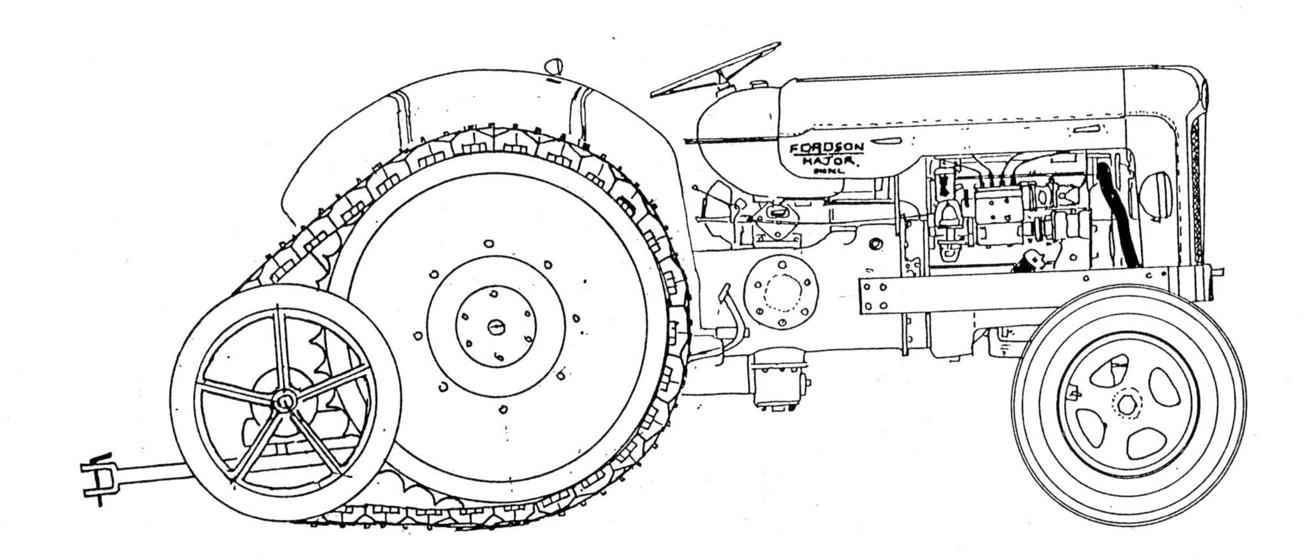

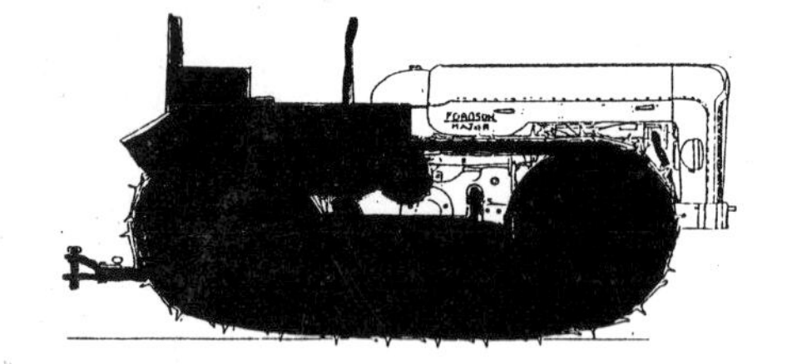

1952 County Crawler.

With track design inherited from the E27N the County Crawler continued in production throughout the 'life' of the New Fordson Major. This is an early example.

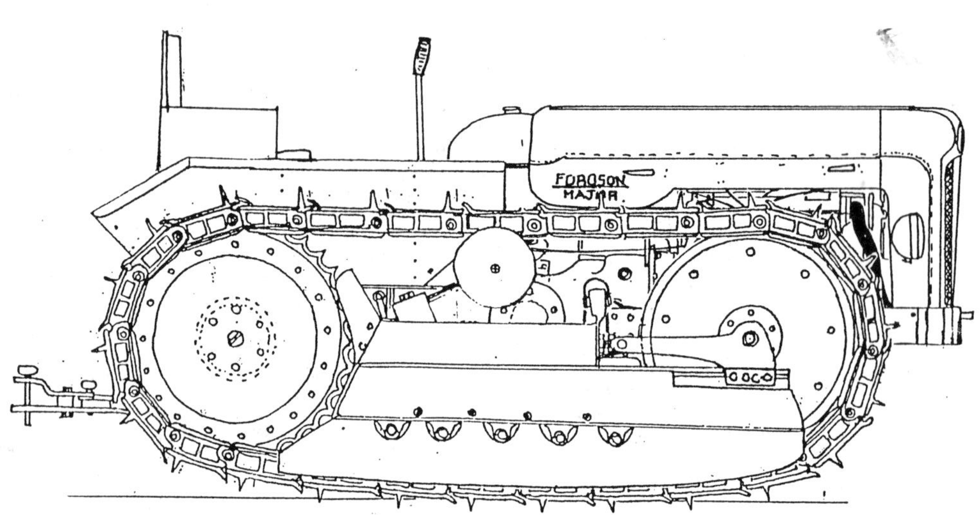

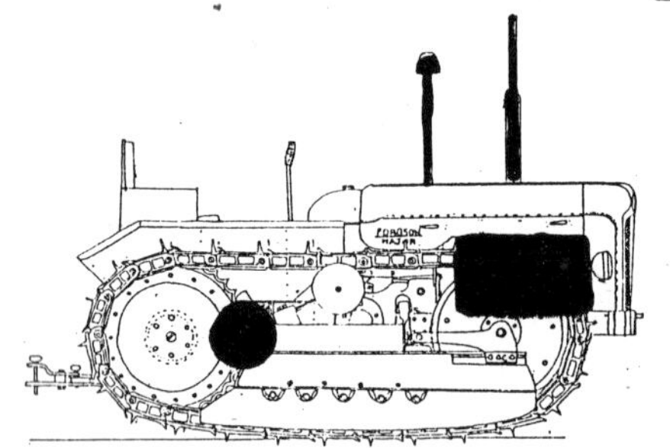

1957 County Crawler Mark II.

The Mark II model launched in 1957 featured improved steering clutches and the engine was hidden by side panels.

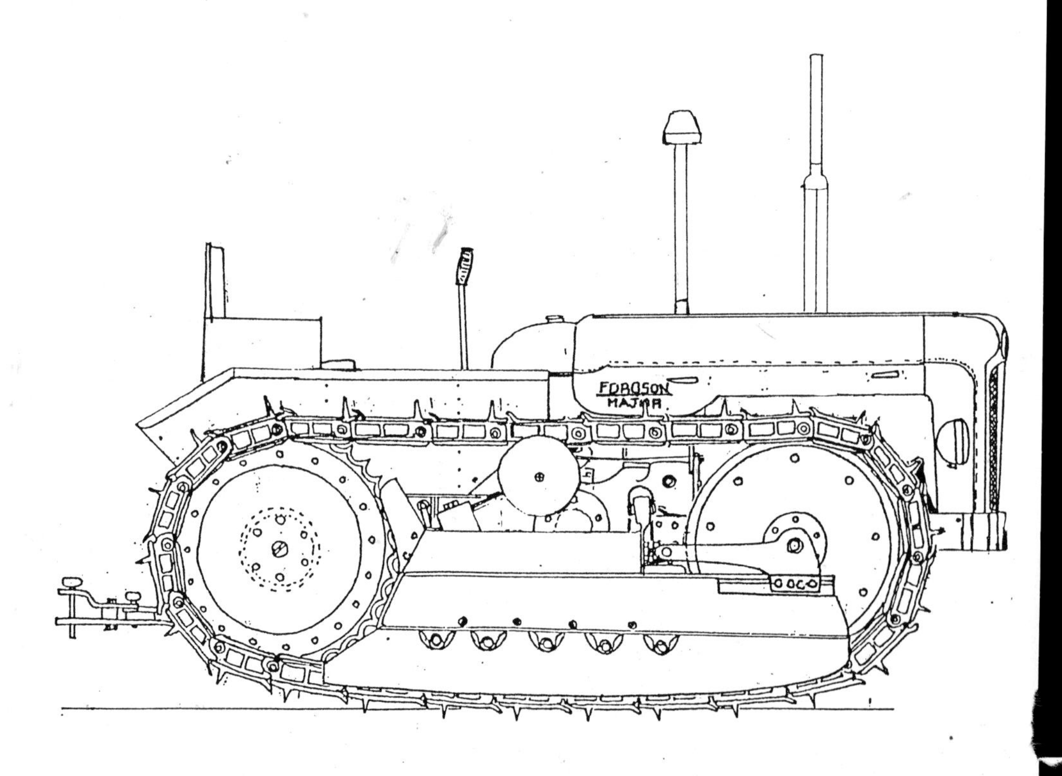

Serial Number and Casting Code locations.

These diagrams show the location of serial numbers and casting code numbers which are detailed on the next two pages. Readers may photocopy these pages to record details of their own tractors; or forms are available from the publisher on receipt of a large S.A.E. We ask owners to send us copies of their forms to assist in further research.
The first drawing shows locations of some casting codes and the engine number up to February 1956.

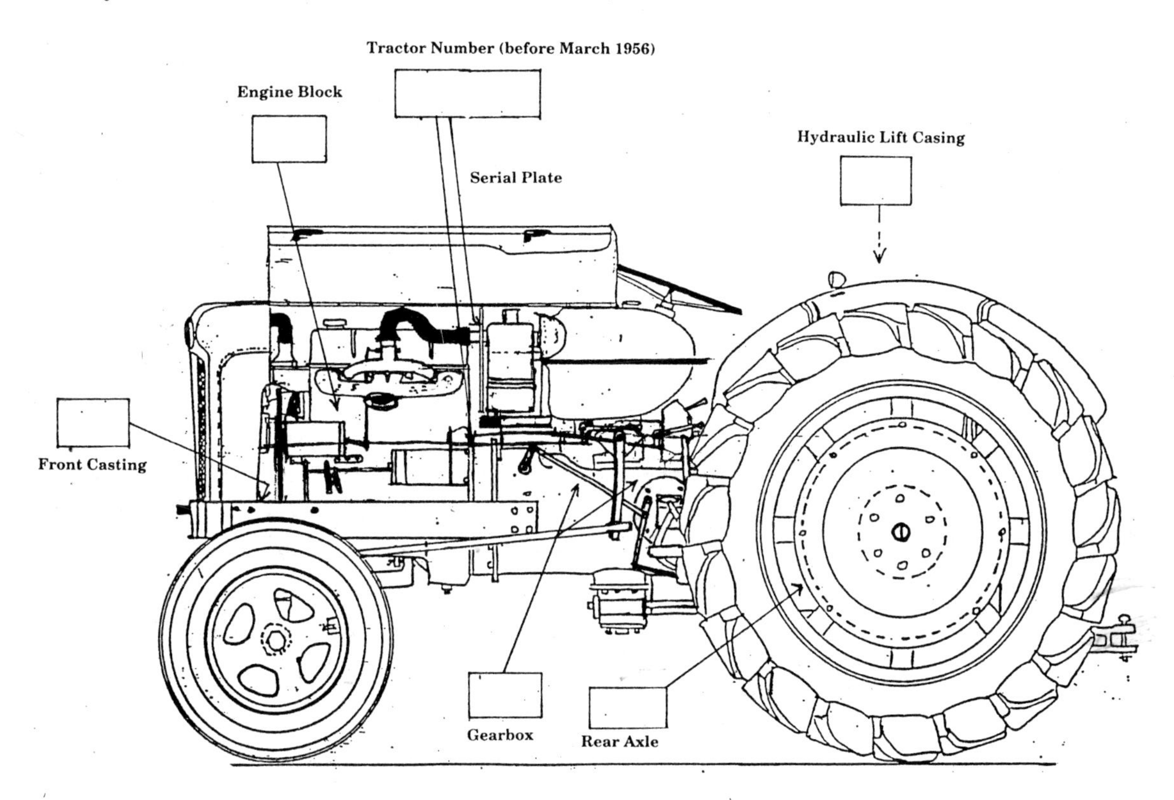

The engine number from March 1956 is seen in the second drawing.

Casting codes consist of a Month prefix letter/date/ year suffix letter until June 1963, thereafter a year number/month letter/date.

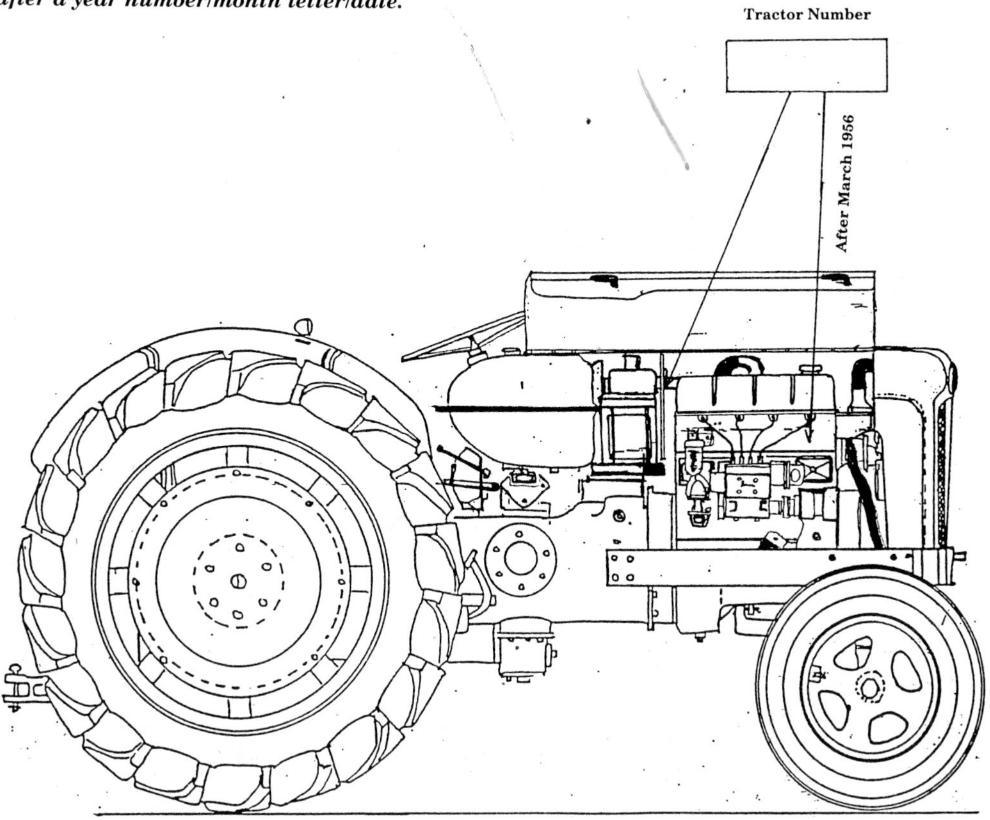

Casting Codes

Month (to 1963) (prefix)		1963 on (year/letter/date)
January	A	A
February	B	B
March	C	C
April	D	D
May	F	E
June	H	F
July	J	G
August	K	H
September	L	K
October	M	L
November	N	M
December	P	N

Year	Code
1951	S
1952	T
1953	U
1954	V
1955	X
1956	Z
1957	A
1958	B
1959	C
1960	D
1961	F
1962	H
1963	J
1963	3 (from June)
1964	4

E1A Model. Production Breakdown 1951-7.

Built up:				Knocked Down:			Grand
Year	Total	S.i.	Diesel	Total	S.i.	Diesel	Total
1951	3	3					3
1952	29032	15100	13932	1412	1132	280	30444
1953	25199	4364	20835	4376	2800	1576	29575
1954	36883	2069	34814	8806	2340	6466	45689
1955	39986	877	39109	8886	380	8506	48872
1956	33860	1722	32138	7131	180	6951	40991
1957	38227	980	37247	7744	60	7684	45971
Totals	203190	25115	178075	38355	6892	31463	241545

Analysed information is not available after this date.

Serial Number location. Up to tractor No. 1380938 on lh. flywheel housing near starter motor.
Tractor No. 1380939 onwards, on a pad on the front rh. side of the engine block. The serial number can also be found on a plate on the bulkhead between the engine and battery compartment.